G

and

COSMOS

GOD
and
COSMOS

*A Christian View of
Time, Space, and
the Universe*

John Byl

THE BANNER OF TRUTH TRUST

THE BANNER OF TRUTH TRUST
3 Murrayfield Road, Edinburgh EH12 6EL, UK
P O Box 621, Carlisle, PA 17013, USA

*

© John Byl 2001
ISBN 0 85151 800 1

*

Typeset in 11/13 pt Sabon MT at
the Banner of Truth Trust
Printed in Great Britain by
Bell & Bain Ltd.,
Glasgow

To My Wife Margaret

'Rejoice with the wife
of thy youth'
(Prov. 5:18)

Contents

FIGURES

Preface

In recent times much has been written about the relation between science and religion. A rather small fraction of this has dealt specifically with interactions between cosmology and theology. Most books discussing this topic assume the validity of modern cosmology and, as a result, propose various modifications to orthodox Christianity. The very few more theologically conservative, creationist works generally have a very narrow focus, being primarily concerned either with disproving big-bang cosmology or with promoting their own particular alternative cosmology.

The purpose of this book is to probe beneath the usual questions of origins, digging deeper into various underlying philosophical issues and examining also a number of closely-related matters. The emphasis will be on the theological presuppositions and implications of modern cosmology on the one hand, and, on the other, the significance of the Bible for cosmology.

This books is addressed to anyone concerned with defending the Christian faith in an age of naturalistic science. In order to be accessible to the general reader, I assume no prior technical knowledge of cosmology. Although specific cosmological models tend to be highly mathematical, this book contains no mathematical equations.

I am grateful to my colleague Rick Sutcliffe who read and critiqued some of the earlier chapters. I thank Douglas Taylor of the Banner of Truth Trust for his helpful suggestions. I am also obliged to Trinity Western University for granting a sabbatical leave during which I did much of my reading and research.

Earlier versions of several portions of this book have appeared previously in various publications. Much of the material in Chapter 1 appeared in 'Preliminary considerations: on scientific and theological method', *Premise*, vol. 5, no. 3, pp. 1–11, 1998 (http://capo.org/premise/archive.html). Parts of Chapter 3 appeared in 'The role of beliefs in modern cosmology', J. M. van der Meer (ed.), *Facets of Faith and Science, Vol. 3: The Role of Beliefs in the Natural Sciences,* Lanham: University Press of America, 1996, pp. 47–62. Parts of Chapter 4 were published as 'On Craig's defence of the Kalam Cosmological Argument' in Volume 4 of the same series, *Interpreting God's Action in the World,* pp. 75–90. They are used here with the permission of the publisher. The first part of Chapter 5 was published in 'On Life in the Universe', *Professorenforum-Journal,* Vol. 2, No. 1, January 2001 (http://www.professorenforum. de/volumes).

JOHN BYL
January 2001

The Basic Questions

Can a Christian living in the space age still believe in heaven,
angels, and life after death, or has modern scientific knowledge
disproved such naïve notions? Does the big-bang theory provide
evidence for a Creator, or does it cast doubt upon Genesis?

Christians are being increasingly confronted with such disturbing
questions. The aim of this study is to examine some of the deeper
issues lurking behind these problems. Our investigations will take us
into the realms of cosmology and theology. *Cosmology* is the science
concerned with the study of the physical universe as a whole (we
shall consider it to include *cosmogony*, the study of the origin of the
universe); *theology* is the study of God and his revelation.

How do theology and cosmology affect each other? To what extent
is cosmology influenced by theological biases? What, if any, theological consequences can be drawn from cosmology? Such questions will
form the focus of this study. We shall limit ourselves primarily to
Christian theology, taking the Bible as the prime source of divine
revelation.

For Christians a major issue is that of what the Bible has to say
regarding cosmology. The Bible certainly seems to address itself quite
specifically to the origin and destiny of the universe, as well as to the
existence of a spiritual world. In medieval times a detailed cosmology
was constructed, based, it was thought, on such biblical information.

In modern times the situation has changed. The old medieval
picture of the universe has long since been discarded. It has been
replaced by a new dominant cosmology: *big-bang cosmology*. This

theory postulates that the physical universe, with all its contents, was caused by the initial explosion (the big bang), and subsequent development, of a highly compressed ball of energy-matter.

Reconciling Cosmology and the Bible

How is this modern cosmology to be reconciled with Christianity? Christians have reacted with a rather wide range of opinion. It is clear that big-bang cosmology is at odds with the traditional interpretation of the Bible. The acceptance of big-bang cosmology thus requires a new look at those biblical texts that appear to have cosmological implications.

One possible approach is that of *concordism*, which strives to reinterpret the Bible so as to bring it into harmony with modern cosmology. Indeed, some authors claim that the big bang actually confirms Genesis, if only we read it properly.

Others, convinced that such concordist interpretations are invalid, may adopt more drastic methods. Perhaps the Bible, written in a pre-scientific age, is in error when it addresses scientific matters. Perhaps the Bible is concerned only with theological matters. A view that has recently become quite popular is that of *complementarianism*, which sees cosmology and theology as totally independent, each dealing with different matters: they give *complementary* descriptions of the same reality. Theology is considered to be concerned with questions of *Who* and *Why*; science deals with matters of *When* and *How*.

In short, adapting the Bible to big-bang cosmology seems to entail either stretching its interpretation or curtailing its authority.

An alternative approach is to adapt cosmology to the Bible, or at least, to the traditional reading of the Bible as it has been accepted by the vast majority of Christians throughout the ages. As this implies the rejection of big-bang cosmology, questions must now in turn be asked regarding the status and authority of cosmological theories: How well established is big-bang cosmology, and is it possible to construct viable, Bible-based alternative cosmologies?

Evaluating Cosmological Models

Most astronomers – and also many theologians – are convinced that the big-bang theory is essentially correct. In a subsequent chapter we shall examine in some detail the strengths and weaknesses of this dominant cosmological theory. At this point I wish to raise only a few preliminary concerns.

In constructing a cosmological theory, or 'model' (that is, a simplified mathematical representation) of the origin and structure of the entire universe it is clear that we have only very limited observational data at our disposal. It is only in the last seventy years or so that we have observed very distant galaxies. And it may well be that even what we can presently observe forms only a small fraction of the whole universe.

To draw general conclusions regarding the whole universe from a limited set of data necessarily requires that we make some theoretical assumptions. Similar considerations apply to the history of the universe. For example, we cannot directly observe the big bang, which supposedly occurred some fifteen billion years ago. Such a hypothetical past event can only be inferred on the basis of data, in the form of light rays, which we receive now.

Moreover, as we shall see, the data are explicable in a number of different ways. Can we be certain, for example, that the physical laws applicable here and now are valid universally? Perhaps the constant of gravity or the speed of light varies in space and time. A number of such proposals can be found in professional astronomical journals. Or perhaps the entire universe was created instantaneously, in the not-too-distant past. While such a possibility may strike us as rather unlikely, it is notoriously difficult to disprove. In short, there exist a host of possible theoretical extensions and explanations of the astronomical observations.

Given such a large choice of theories, how can we hope to stumble upon the correct theory? Indeed, even if we were to chance upon the best theory, how could we recognize it as such? Or, for that matter, how can we even choose the better of only two competing theories?

Within the last half century it has come to be quite generally accepted that scientific theories cannot be simply deduced from observations. On the contrary, the origin of scientific theories is now considered to be largely subjective. The noted philosopher of science Sir Karl Popper asserts that 'we must regard all laws or theories as hypothetical or conjectural; that is, as guesses'[1]; he sees theories as

---

[1] *Objective Knowledge*, London: Oxford University Press, 1972, p. 9.

'the free creations of our minds'.[1] Or, as Carl Hempel puts it:

> The transition from data to theory requires creative imagination. Scientific hypotheses and theories are not derived from observed facts, but are invented in order to account for them.[2]

It seems that theories are not so much *given to* us by nature as *imposed by* us on nature; they are not so much the result of rational thought as the creations of our irrational intuition.

While one might think that further research would falsify the majority of such theories, this is not easily done in practice. A favoured theory, such as big-bang cosmology, can always be saved from observational disproof by making suitable modifications to it. A theory that must be supported by artificial, *ad hoc* devices (designed specifically to overcome particular shortcomings) is generally not highly ranked in terms of plausibility. Nevertheless, however difficult it may be to demonstrate a particular *ad hoc* theory to be true, it is even harder to conclusively disprove it. According to Imre Lakatos:

> Scientific theories are not only equally unprovable, and equally improbable, but they are also equally undisprovable.[3]

While recognizing that there was no logic to the *discovery* of theories, Popper hoped to construct a rational process for the objective *selection* of theories. He proposed that genuine scientific theories should be *falsifiable* (that is, they should make definite testable predictions). However, if we were to apply this criterion to cosmology we would have little theory left. Currently virtually all cosmological models are falsified by observations. Nor does Popper offer any justification as to why easily falsifiable theories are more likely to be true than others.

It is, of course, possible to play the game of cosmology under different rules. Various criteria for assessing theories have been suggested. For example, Howard van Till[4] lists cognitive relevance, predictive accuracy, coherence, explanatory scope, unifying power,

---

[1] *Conjectures and Refutations*, London: Routledge, 1962, p. 192.
[2] *Philosophy of Natural Science*, Englewood Cliffs, N.J.: Prentice-Hall, 1966, p. 15.
[3] *The Methodology of Research Programmes*, Cambridge: The University Press, 1980, p. 19.
[4] *Portraits of Creation*, Grand Rapids: Eerdmans, 1990, p. 146.

and fertility. Yet, while such criteria may seem reasonable enough, it is generally granted that they are by no means rigorous. They merely reflect values used in practice. Indeed, the creation of selection criteria is no less subjective than the creation of scientific theories. As Lakatos notes (p.122):

> These scientific games are without genuine epistemological [having to do with knowledge] content unless we superimpose on them some sort of metaphysical principle which will say that the game, as specified by the methodology, gives us the best chance of approaching the truth.

In short, science in general – and cosmology in particular – is plagued by the lack of definite, objective criteria that might allow us to easily separate true theories from false ones. It is at this crucial point that we must often be guided by extra-scientific factors.

The Role of Religious Commitments

This brings us to the question as to what role religious commitments should play in cosmological theorizing. How should religious beliefs influence cosmology?

It is clear that in practice, at least, religious beliefs can play a decisive role in the creation, assessment, and selection of cosmological theories. For example, the choice for or against the big bang is sometimes made on the basis of religious grounds. Thus Fred Hoyle rejects big-bang cosmology at least in part because the sudden appearance of the universe at a finite time in the past seems to him to imply a supernatural cause,[1] while, on the same grounds, Christians such as Norman Geisler[2] and Hugh Ross[3] are favourably inclined towards the big bang.

Or consider the rejection by creationists of a long evolutionary history of the universe. This is based primarily on their religious commitment to the Bible. On the other hand, the National Academy of Science in the U.S.A. has objected to creationism primarily on the grounds that creationism 'subordinates evidence to statements made on authority and revelation'[4] and that 'it accounts for the origin of

[1] *Astronomy and Cosmology*, San Francisco: Freeman, 1975, p. 684.
[2] *Journal of the Evangelical Theological Society*, 1979, 22, p. 282.
[3] *The Fingerprint of God*, Orange: Promise Pub. Co., 2nd edition.
[4] *Scientific Creationism: A View from the National Academy of Science*, Washington: National Academy Press, 1984.

life by supernatural means'. This prompt rejection of revelation and the supernatural is likewise a religious choice. In this regard it is notable that modern cosmology is marked by a pervasive naturalism that leaves little room for any religion in the traditional sense.

Are such religious commitments legitimate? Howard Van Till contends that extra-scientific dogma should not influence our assessments and selection of theories:

> Religious commitments, whether theistic or nontheistic, should not be permitted to interfere with the normal functioning of the epistemic value system developed and employed within the scientific community. Great mischief is done when extrascientific dogma is allowed to take precedence over epistemic values such as cognitive relevance, predictive accuracy . . . Science held hostage to any belief system, whether naturalistic or theistic, can no longer function effectively to gain knowledge of the physical universe . . . Science held hostage by extrascientific dogma is science made barren.[1]

Van Till's exclusion of religious commitments from the selection of scientific theories follows from his presupposition that science and religion complement each other, each being sovereign in its own domain. But even this consideration, like all standards for theory selection, is itself based on extra-scientific considerations.

At heart we cannot avoid being guided by religious and philosophical factors in our assessment and selection of theories. However much one might wish to eliminate the supernatural from science, it is quite another matter to prove that it actually is absent from reality. The universe beyond our observations may be quite different from our preferred cosmological model.

It is undeniable that religious and philosophical prejudices have at times blinded their adherents to blatant deficiencies in favoured theories and to obvious advantages in rival models. It is thus important that such presuppositions be made very explicit. To minimize undue distortion and bias, our premises and criteria should at least be stated openly.

Epistemology and Revelation

Given the importance of presuppositions, the most basic question is that of our *epistemology* (our theory of knowledge): how should we

---

[1] *Portraits of Creation*, p. 149.

rate the various sources of knowledge? More specifically, how should we rate divine revelation as a source of cosmological knowledge?

One could, for example, adopt the orthodox position that the Bible is the inerrant Word of God and that the traditional interpretation is the intended one. Granted the premise of an omniscient God who has revealed truth to us, it follows that divine revelation should speak authoritatively on all it addresses. Such a divine source of knowledge would carry more epistemological weight than mere speculative theorizing, with its subjective criteria and assessments. It follows from such an epistemology that cosmological theories should be selected so as to be consistent with Scripture.

One objection that has been voiced against the orthodox position is its limited view of divine revelation. Christians have long distinguished between God's *special* revelation (the Bible) and his *general* revelation (history and nature). God, it has been said, reveals himself through both his Word and his works.

In the traditional view, however, general revelation consists only of God's *self*-revelation. Through his works of creation and providence the invisible character of God is made known (see, for example, *Rom.* 1:20). After the Fall, man's knowledge of God through general revelation has been darkened by sin, so that Scripture and the grace of the Holy Spirit are now needed for man to understand properly the message of general revelation.

Those who reject this view often justify this by appealing to a more expanded assessment of general revelation. For example, David W. Diehl has urged that general revelation should include not only knowledge of God, but also that of his works in nature.[1] He has in mind both observations of nature and scientific theorizing that goes beyond the observations. According to Diehl, some scientific views that have been unpopular with theologians are so well-established that it would be truly unscientific and unfair to general revelation to reject them. Special and general revelation should, asserts Diehl, have equal authority, each having final authority within its own territory.

What are we to make of this? To be sure, few would deny the importance of our *observations* of nature. In this sense *general revelation* (I would prefer the term *creation* or *nature* here) is surely

[1] 'Evangelicalism and general revelation: an unfinished agenda', *The Journal of the Evangelical Theological Society*, 1987, *30*, p. 441.

authoritative: we must appeal to it, or at least our experiences of it, as a check on all our scientific theorizing.

Further, we must rely on the rules of deductive logic. It is evident that God has made the universe in such a way that these rules apply. God has endowed man, created in his image, with the analytical abilities to use these laws, although man, due to his finite, fallen nature, can make logical mistakes.

However, our reasoning powers are not confined to the mere application of logic but include also the ability for imaginative, theoretical thought. Unfortunately, particularly after the Fall, our reasoning is a tool that is controlled by our inner desires. As such it can easily be misguided: 'For out of the heart come evil thoughts' (*Matt.* 15:19). Clearly, man is responsible for his thoughts and hence also for their products, including scientific theories. After all, as we have seen, scientific theories are but the speculative inventions of man's creative imagination.

A proper epistemology will thus give high weight to Scripture, observations, and logic. These are all God-given and will thus be in harmony; they form the touchstone of our knowledge. On the other hand, human theorizing, in all its forms, is in a much lower category of knowledge. If it fails the test of logic, observation, and Scripture then we can reject it as certainly false. Even if it passes this test we must be cautious: any claim that goes beyond observation and Scripture is still likely to be false.

The difficulty with Diehl's position, as I have argued in more detail elsewhere[1], arises when he extends the contents of 'general revelation' beyond observational data and logic to include also scientific theories. If, as Diehl believes, general revelation is infallible, then such infallibility must also be granted to certain scientific theories. But which ones? The history of science is filled with many examples of scientific theories, now discarded, that were once held as undoubted truths. The most famous such case is that of Newtonian mechanics, which was for centuries considered as absolutely true but which has now been dethroned by Einstein's theory of relativity. Unfortunately, Diehl offers no criteria by which we can distinguish true theories from false ones, or even judge relative correctness.

---

[1] 'General Revelation and Evangelicalism', *Mid-America Journal of Theology,* 1989, 5, pp. 1–13.

Already from the beginning of the scientific revolution, the notion that God has revealed truth in two books, Scripture and nature, has been widely used as a means of reconciling science and Scripture. Historically, however, the doctrine of the two books has led to a decline in biblical authority. Once we allow the premise that some scientific theories can be taken as divine truth, we are in essence permitting the 'book of science' to modify Scripture. In the absence of valid criteria by which we can devise and detect correct theories, our reading of the Bible will be forever in a state of flux, depending on which scientific theories are currently in vogue.

In short, a major problem in reconciling science and Scripture is what we can refer to as *the problem of scientific knowledge*: we have no justifiably valid criteria for finding true theories. The only place where it is relatively easy to draw a line is between observations and theories that are devised to explain or extend the observations. I say here 'relatively' since even our observations are to some degree theory-laden. For example, our theories determine what aspects of reality are to be observed. Yet, even so, our observations are still much more secure than their theoretical extrapolations. We can accept as scientific facts only the actual observed data. Once we step beyond the observations we are set adrift in a sea of subjective speculation.

Interpreting the Bible

Thus far I have defended the notion that religious commitments may influence cosmological theorizing and that relevant divine revelation should be limited to special revelation. But what does the Bible have to say on cosmological matters? How are we to interpret those passages that seem to deal with this issue? What hermeneutical principles should be employed?

The question of the proper interpretation of Scripture has been disputed from the early days of Christianity. Augustine, and later Aquinas, argued that we should take the Bible in its literal sense, unless internal scriptural evidence shows conclusively that a non-literal interpretation is required. As to the claims of natural knowledge, these were to be over-ridden by Scripture unless they could be proven to be true. The lightest word of God was to have precedence over the heaviest word of man unless the latter could be conclusively demonstrated. In that case, since God's Word cannot conflict with the truth, it is evident that another interpretation is required.

But what would constitute a valid proof of the correctness of any item of extra-biblical knowledge? Since the sixteenth century, with the advancement of scientific investigation, various aspects of the traditional interpretation of Scripture have been challenged: for example, its apparent geocentricity, the account of Noah's flood, biblical chronology, the story of Adam and Eve, and the existence of heaven and spiritual beings. Some Christians have held on to the literal reading of Scripture, denying that the new scientific ideas had been adequately demonstrated. Most, however, felt the need to modify their reading of Scripture, at least to some degree.

At first the troublesome portions of Scripture were merely reinterpreted so as to be reconciled with modern learning. Elastic methods of interpretation were advocated. To take just one typical example of this concordist school, consider Davis Young, a Christian geologist, who writes:

> We need not twist or misinterpret the facts in order to get agreement between the Bible and science. Christians must realize that the Scriptures do not require us to believe in six twenty-four-hour days of creation. There is legitimate internal biblical evidence to indicate that the days of creation may have been indefinite periods of time. Moreover, the genealogies of Genesis 5 and 11 need not be taken in a rigidly literal fashion . . . It is not entirely clear that the Bible is talking about a geographically universal flood . . . There is considerable room for legitimate variation of interpretation of the creation and the flood.[1]

The obvious difficulty with such a flexible approach to Scripture is the danger of merely reading out of it what we put in. Scripture is reduced to a mirror of human thoughts rather than a source of divine light.

The inadequacies of concordism have been stressed by none other than Young himself in a more recent work, where he repudiates his earlier concordistic position:

> All the variations of the concordist theme give us a Bible that is constantly held hostage to the latest scientific theorizing. Texts are twisted,

[1] *Christianity and the Age of the Earth*, Grand Rapids: Zondervan, 1982, p. 152.

pulled, poked, stretched, and prodded to 'agree' with scientific conclusions, so that concordism today undermines honest, Christian
exegesis.[1]

In short, concordism is inconsistent with an epistemology that
stresses the supremacy of God's Word. It is crucial that we adopt a
hermeneutic that is not unduly influenced by human theorizing. If we
are to listen to God's Word with an open ear, then we must strive to
interpret the text objectively, applying sound hermeneutical principles. The most direct, natural interpretation is thus generally to be
preferred, unless internal scriptural evidence indicates otherwise.

The Scope of Biblical Authority

It is noteworthy that Young comes to the conclusion that, leaving
aside extra-biblical considerations, the literal interpretation of
Genesis is, after all, exegetically preferred. Nevertheless, he believes
that the weight of scientific evidence is such that the literal reading
cannot be true. Having rejected concordism, Young opts for what
amounts to a limitation of biblical authority. He advocates that we
treat Genesis 1, not as a scientific or historical report, but as a piece
of ancient literature with well-defined thought patterns, structures,
symbols and images, intended to convey theological truths.[2]

In recent years the nature and extent of biblical authority has been
much discussed also in evangelical circles. One increasingly popular
position is that science and Scripture do not *contradict* each other,
but *complement* each other. Howard Van Till, a Christian astronomer and a colleague of Young, has vigorously supported this point
of view. As we have already noted, Van Till believes that science
should be religiously neutral. The evolutionary and biblical views of
the cosmos are complementary descriptions that answer different
types of questions. Science reveals information about the physical
structure and past history of the universe; the Bible tells us about its
relation to God. Science answers questions of 'how' and 'when'; the
Bible answers questions about 'who' and 'why'.[3]

---

[1] 'Scripture in the hands of geologists', *Westminster Theological Journal,* 1987,
  49, p. 6.
[2] *Ibid.,* p. 303.
[3] *The Fourth Day,* Grand Rapids: Eerdmans, pp. 193–215

The difficulty with this solution is that the Bible itself does not suggest that its authority is limited to theological questions of 'who' or 'why'. On the contrary, it seems at times to speak rather specifically on such matters, also regarding the origin of the physical universe. On what grounds, then, can we set a boundary to its authority, and how can we determine where the boundary would be?

Van Till tries to draw a line by distinguishing between the *divine contents* of a biblical story and the *human packaging* in which it comes. The theological thrust of a biblical passage can be taken as trustworthy, but not the specific physical details that form the 'packaging'. He explains:

> So we as readers of Scripture must be studiously and prayerfully wise in separating the contents (the trustworthy teachings of God) from the vehicle and packaging. Neglecting that separation would be as foolish as attempting to eat a granola bar without first removing it from its wrapper.[1]

Yet one may well ask how Van Till can be so certain that the 'packaging' is not divinely inspired as well. How, in the absence of clear, divinely ratified criteria can we ever hope to disentangle the divine message from the allegedly human wrappings? Ultimately the discernment of the divine teachings contained in Scripture is left to the subjective whims of the individual reader.

Of course, there are other options beyond the above categories of concordism and complementarianism. One could consider Scripture and science to be either more or less interdependent. However, to the extent that these involve a reduction in biblical authority, the same considerations apply.

We conclude that whereas concordism unduly distorted the biblical message by its elastic hermeneutics, complementarianism distorts it by imposing unwarranted limits on biblical authority. Those who wish to modify the traditional reading of Scripture are plagued with the lack of clear, valid criteria for separating the wheat from the alleged chaff. As it has been said, if we cannot accept all of Scripture as authoritative, how can we be sure any of it is?

It should be noted that the affirmation of the epistemological supremacy of Scripture implies its inerrancy. If we accept Scripture as

[1] *Ibid.*, pp. 15–16.

the highest standard, then there is no means to test its accuracy; inerrancy must be assumed from the start. If we follow the principle that Scripture must interpret Scripture, then our interpretation of Scripture should be internally consistent. There should be no internal contradictions. Of course, since the Bible does make specific predictions regarding the future, biblical claims are ultimately testable. Meanwhile, however, we must resist the temptation to 'prove' inerrancy by appealing to scientific evidence, for that in effect makes the scientist, fallible man that he is, the judge of Scripture. Inerrancy must be our starting point, not our conclusion.

Is the traditional interpretation of an all-authoritative Scripture tenable in our scientific age? That is the prime question to be addressed in the chapters ahead. It is noteworthy that, if scientific 'facts' are to be limited to direct observations, there will be little actual conflict between the Bible and scientific knowledge. After all, the Bible is concerned with events in the distant past, in the (as yet unobserved) future, and in the (unseen) spiritual realm; scientific observations concern only the present and the very recent past. Clashes arise primarily between the Bible and scientific *theorizing*. The fundamental question that must be posed is, therefore, whether the scientific theories of modern cosmology, uncertain as they may be, are nevertheless sufficiently established to warrant their elevation above Scripture.

Preview

Having dealt with preliminary considerations regarding science and Scripture, let me briefly sketch out our course for the remainder of this book. Our study will focus on two basic questions:

1. What does theology have to say to cosmology?
How have theological considerations influenced the construction, assessment, and selection of cosmological theories? What does the Bible have to say regarding cosmology?

2. What does cosmology have to say to theology?
How have cosmological models influenced theology? What theological consequences can be drawn from big-bang cosmology? How reliable are cosmological models?

We shall begin, in the next chapter, with a brief examination of medieval cosmology, its theological connections, and the factors that led from it to modern cosmology. In the following chapter big-bang cosmology will be analysed. Its strengths, weaknesses, and underlying assumptions will be discussed. Various alternative cosmological interpretations of the observational evidence will be presented.

The next chapters examine various theological implications that have been drawn from big-bang cosmology. Cosmological evidence has been used in a number of proofs for the existence of God. The validity of such proofs is the topic of one chapter. Another chapter deals with the future of the universe, particularly with regard to life. The possibility of extra-terrestrial life will be examined. Supporters of modern cosmology have proposed a variety of gods allegedly more feasible in the modern world than the Christian God. These strange gods, and the hope they might present for a life hereafter, will be discussed in a further chapter.

Next we examine what the Bible has to say regarding cosmological matters. This is followed by a chapter examining a variety of cosmological models that are built upon biblical givens. The validity and function of such models are discussed, particularly with an eye on their usefulness as an apologetic tool. A final chapter summarizes the conclusions reached.

2

A Brief Historical Sketch

We shall first make a quick survey of the history of cosmology. Our main focus will be on medieval cosmology, a very ambitious combination of science and theology. To provide some background we shall look first at ancient cosmology, particularly that of the Greeks. Later we shall examine the demise of medieval cosmology and the subsequent cosmological developments up to the beginning of the twentieth century.

Ancient Cosmology

All ancient civilizations had their cosmologies, their notions as to how the world came to be and how it was structured. Throughout history man has been concerned with understanding and explaining the world that he experiences.

The first man, Adam, no doubt knew quite well how God had created the universe. Various details are still preserved for us in the creation account of Genesis, which formed the basis for Jewish cosmology. Other ancient cosmologies are to a large extent distortions of the original creation story. The creation myths of Mesopotamia and Egypt, dating back to at least 2000 BC, both describe the world as beginning as a watery abyss, from which gradually emerged a blind, formless spirit. The mingling of this spirit and the watery abyss produced the various gods and goddesses, as well as the contents of the present world. The prime functions of these gods were to serve and to protect mankind.

In addition to his interest in the origin of the universe, ancient man was also a keen observer of the universe, particularly the starry heavens. The Babylonians, for example, had already by 2000 BC divided the sky into the constellations of the Zodiac, compiled star catalogues and recorded the movements of the planets. They were able to predict eclipses and to prepare calendars to forecast the seasons and the times of full moon. However, they did not attempt to explain their celestial observations in terms of cosmological theories or models. They collected many observations but did not unify these by way of theoretical principles.

Origins of Greek Cosmology

Scientific models of the universe first arose out of Greek thought. The Greek philosophers rejected magic and myth; they strove to provide naturalistic explanations for the universe. Relying heavily on careful observation and critical thought, they devised simplified mathematical models of the universe. These are still the fundamental elements of science as practised today.

The origin of science and philosophy is often traced to Thales (621–543 BC), a native of Miletus in Ionia. Thales achieved fame in 585 BC by predicting a solar eclipse. He reduced the multiplicity of the universe to a unity by postulating that all things were ultimately composed of the same, all-pervading substance: water. According to Thales the world evolved out of water by purely natural means.

Anaximander, a younger associate of Thales, rejected the notion that water was the basic element of the universe. He postulated that all things consisted of combinations of four substances: water, air, fire, and earth. These elements were in turn derived from a more basic substance called *apeiron*, meaning *boundless*. In the beginning there was only *apeiron*. Air, fire, earth and water were formed from the primordial *apeiron* by means of a whirling motion, through which the various elements were separated. This whirling principle at the same time explained the motions of the stars. In the centre of the universe was the earth, which was cylindrical in shape. Man lived on one of its flat faces.

From these beginnings the Greeks constructed a host of cosmological models. Generally they strove to explain the universe in terms of some key fundamental element, physical principle, or numerical concept. Many of the Greeks held that the universe was the product of, or under the guidance of, a rational intelligence. Yet there were some who rejected any notion of divinity.

The latter group contained, in particular, the atomists Leucippus (5th century BC) and his disciple Democritus (5th–4th century BC). Leucippus believed that the universe consisted of only two things: atoms and empty space. The atoms, infinite in number, moved through infinite space; collisions between atoms resulted in the formation of new objects. Eventually the various objects decayed back into individual atoms. This universe of endless worlds was in a constant state of flux, producing an unlimited variety of objects. Asserting that the universe had existed since eternity, the atomists tried to avoid the need not only for a designer, but also for a creator.

While the atomist model had a distinctly modern flavour, it had little effect on medieval cosmology. Indeed, in spite of the vast variety of Greek cosmology, the only system that heavily influenced medieval cosmology was that deriving from the two greatest ancient philosophers: Plato (427–347 BC) and his pupil Aristotle (384–322 BC).

Classic Cosmology

The essential features of Plato's cosmological system were presented in his book *Timaeus*. Plato believed that the Creator made the universe according to a rational plan. By this time it had become commonly accepted – at least by philosophers – that the earth was a sphere. The earthly sphere was placed in the centre of the universe (see *Figure* 2.1). It was formed from earth, water, air and fire. Around the earth were seven planetary spheres and an eighth outer sphere for the stars. The outer sphere, carrying the stars, rotated daily; the intermediate spheres, carrying the planets, rotated at various rates. The motions of the spheres were caused by intelligent spirits. Everything on earth was imperfect and changing, whereas the heavenly objects were perfect. All things were arranged hierarchically according to their inner dignity and perfection; the whole cosmos bore witness to God's existence and his concern for his creation. According to Plato, the world was not eternal. Rather, it was made by the Creator from a model previously present in his mind. Everything was formed from an initial chaos in accordance with a perfect plan. Also

Figure 2.1: The Geocentric Universe according to Peter Apian, from Apian's *Cosmographicus Liber* (1539). Note the inner spheres of earth and water, air, and fire. (This and other early cosmological diagrams, including *Figures* 2.3 and 2.5–7, appear in S. K. Henninger, *The Cosmological Glass: Renaissance Diagrams of the Universe*, San Marino, Calif.: Huntington Library, 1977).

time itself was created, as the most perfect possible imitation of eternity.

Plato's cosmology was developed further by Aristotle. The inner, sublunar sphere contained the four terrestrial elements of earth, water, air and fire; the rest of the universe was filled with a fifth element called ether. The natural motion of the terrestrial elements was up and down. By this they sought to find their proper places according to weight. The natural motion of the ether was perfect, endless circular motion about the earth.

Since every motion must have a cause, there must be an unmoved prime mover, situated beyond the sphere of the fixed stars. The prime mover set the outer movable sphere in motion. From this sphere motion was transmitted through the various spheres for the heavenly bodies, so that the whole system was kept in motion. Aristotle maintained that the prime mover moves everything else 'by being loved'. Both Plato and Aristotle believed that the order of the universe pointed to the existence of a Creator.

The perfect motion of the ethereal spheres, controlled by intelligent agents, was without beginning or end. In contrast to Plato, Aristotle held that the universe had existed essentially unchanged from eternity. Since the outer boundary rotated about the earth in a finite time (24 hours), it followed that the universe was necessarily finite.

Saving the Phenomena

This ambitious cosmology did, however, have one major deficiency. Whereas the fixed stars did indeed display the prescribed perfect circular motions, the 'wandering' stars (that is, the planets) did not quite follow such simple orbits. Their motions varied significantly from that of uniform speed over perfect circles. This was noted already by Plato, who assigned his students the problem of devising mathematical hypotheses that would 'save the appearances'. Thus astronomers were set the task of reconciling theory and practice. How could the complicated motion of the planets be reduced to uniform circular motion? Aristotle tried to solve the problem, but at considerable expense: he needed fifty-five intermediary spheres[1]. Even then his model fell short of the observations.

[1] See N. Max Wildiers, *The Theologian and His Universe*, New York: Seabury Press, 1982.

The problem was eventually solved through the efforts of Claudius Ptolemy in about 150 AD. In doing so Ptolemy invented a number of novel geometrical devices: the *epicycle* (a small circle superimposed upon a larger circle called the *deferent*), the *eccentric* (a device making the centre of the circle rotate off-centre about the earth), and the *equant* (another off-centre point from which speeds were calculated, in order to make the speeds uniform). These concepts are all depicted in *Figure* 2.2. The resulting geometric model worked very well: it yielded results that closely approximated the observed motions and enabled astronomers to predict future planetary positions. However, in the case of some planets it was found necessary to add further epicycles, smaller epicycles moving about larger ones, to describe the observed motions adequately. The complete Ptolemaic system consisted of forty epicycles.

Nevertheless, in spite of its practical success, the model gave no physical explanation of planetary motion. Indeed, in Aristotle's cosmological model of solid spheres rotating about a central earth, motions corresponding to epicycles, eccentrics and equants were physically impossible. Ptolemy defended his mathematical model by adopting an anti-realist (also called 'instrumentalist') view of scientific theories, claiming that astronomical hypotheses were merely useful fictions – or instruments – that enabled one to make practical predictions. His prime criteria in choosing theories were (1) accuracy in 'saving the appearances' and (2) maximum simplicity. Ptolemy believed that physical explanations were necessarily speculative, that philosophers would never agree on them, and that only mathematical models could yield solid conclusions free of doubt.

This view of scientific theorizing was quite different from the rival, 'realist' position that had been defended by Aristotle, who believed that theories should do more than merely fit the observations: they should also be in accord with the true nature of things. Thus his followers rejected Ptolemy's system, since it was contrary to the principles of Aristotle's physics. The struggle between realist and instrumentalist views of scientific theorizing continues up to this day, with the realists claiming that their theories portray deeper truths of reality and the instrumentalists questioning the ability of science to penetrate deeper than the observed phenomena.[1]

[1] For a brief review see John Byl, 'Instrumentalism: A Third Option', *Journal of the American Scientific Affiliation*, 1985, 37, pp. 11–18.

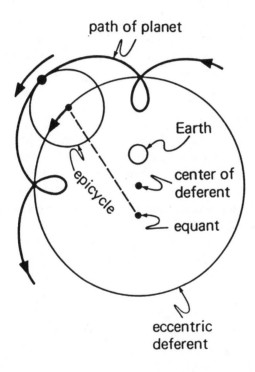

Figure 2.2: Epicyclic Theory: A planet revolves about a small circle, an *epicycle,* which in turn revolves about a larger circle, the *deferent.* The deferent is eccentric when its centre is not the earth. The *equant* is a non-central point about which the epicycle moves at a constant angular rate.

Medieval Cosmology

The early church fathers struggled with the problem of how to reconcile the Bible with the scientific thought of the Greeks. A number of
different approaches were taken. One school of thought, associated
mainly with the Syrian church, adopted a very negative attitude toward Greek cosmology. Insisting that truth was to be found only in
God's Word, they dismissed Greek science and philosophy. On the
other side there were those, particularly in Alexandria, who were
very much impressed with Greek learning. They tried to harmonize
Scripture with pagan teaching. Most popular, however, was a middle-
of-the-road course which made much use of Greek thought but at the
same time held on to the historical sense of Scripture, rejecting pagan
learning where there was a clash. This view was to form the basis for
medieval cosmology.

The Perfect Harmony

Many of the early church fathers saw a great similarity between the
cosmological teachings of Plato and the first chapter of Genesis. Indeed, it was commonly thought that Plato had somehow been
influenced by Moses. In both cases, for example, a single Creator
fashions the cosmos according to a rational plan and the focus of the
universe is upon the man-centred earth.

Plato's cosmology was incorporated within Christian theology
largely through the writings of Pseudo-Dionysius (he claimed his
works were those of the Dionysius converted by Paul in Athens, as
described in Acts 17:34), who wrote around 500 AD. In the Middle
Ages his works were accepted as genuine and became very influential,
being accorded the highest authority after Scripture itself.

Pseudo-Dionysius interpreted Plato's hierarchy of spirits, who
moved the spheres, as angels. He arranged the angels mentioned in
Scripture into a hierarchy of nine orders, one for each heavenly
sphere. His classification lists, in ascending order: angels, archangels
(1 Thess. 4:16), principalities, powers, mights, and dominions (Eph.
1:21), thrones (Col. 1:16), cherubim (Ezek. 10), and seraphim (Isa. 6).
Above the hierarchy of angels, in a tenth sphere, was the abode of
God: the empyrean heaven (see Figures 2.1 and 2.3). The universe
was thus populated with a continuous chain of creatures, stretching

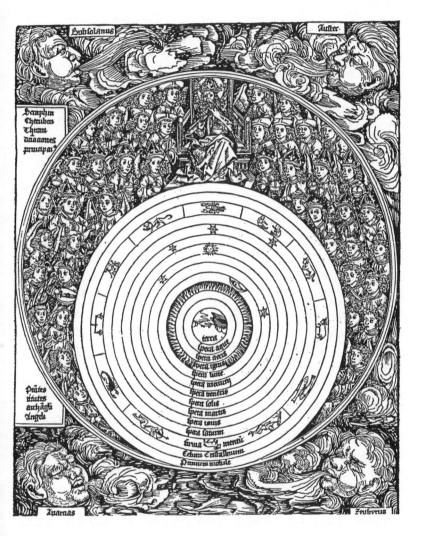

Figure 2.3: The Medieval View of the Universe, from Schedel, *Liber Chronicarum* (1493). Note the nine orders of angels, enumerated at the left, flanking God's throne.

from God, in the highest heaven, to the lowest dweller of hell at the centre of the earth. It should be stressed that medieval man believed the earth to be a globe, and not, as is commonly but erroneously believed, flat. Although in the early Middle Ages there were a few authors who argued for a flat earth, virtually all writers in the later Middle Ages agreed that the earth is a sphere.[1]

Medieval cosmology was brought to its fullest development through the work of Bonaventura (1221–74) and Thomas Aquinas (1224–74). Aquinas in particular was concerned with reconciling the philosophy of Aristotle, whose works had only recently been redis-covered, with Christian theology. The main difficulty with Aristotle was his insistence that the world was eternal. On this point Aquinas affirmed that, although God could have created a universe of eternal duration, God's revelation indicates that the universe began to exist a finite time ago.

In medieval cosmology the universe was considered to be a per-fectly ordered machine. It consisted primarily of a system of spheres which were embedded within each other like the rings of an onion. At the centre was the fixed earth, divided into the four elementary spheres of earth, water, air, and fire. Next came seven spheres con-taining the Moon, Mercury, Venus, the Sun, Mars, Jupiter, and Saturn. These were all encompassed by the three heavenly spheres: one for the stars, one for the crystalline heaven (this referred to the waters of Genesis 1:6), and one for the empyrean, the abode of God. This was essentially the same as Aristotle's cosmos, except that the 'nothingness' beyond the stellar sphere was now replaced with the heavenly dwelling of God.

In line with Plato and Aristotle, it was believed that there was a fundamental difference between the earthly and heavenly spheres. Earthly objects were imperfect and transitory, while the heavenly bodies were perfect and imperishable. The perfection of the heavenly bodies was illustrated by their circular motion, as opposed to the more linear motion of earthly matter. The world consisted of a huge hierarchical structure carefully arranged from the lowest level at the centre of the earth, where hell was located, through the various divisions in society and church, the planetary spheres, to the ultimate perfection of the empyrean (*Figure* 2.4). This world machine was set

[1] C. S. Lewis, *The Discarded Image,* Cambridge: The University Press, 1964, p. 140.

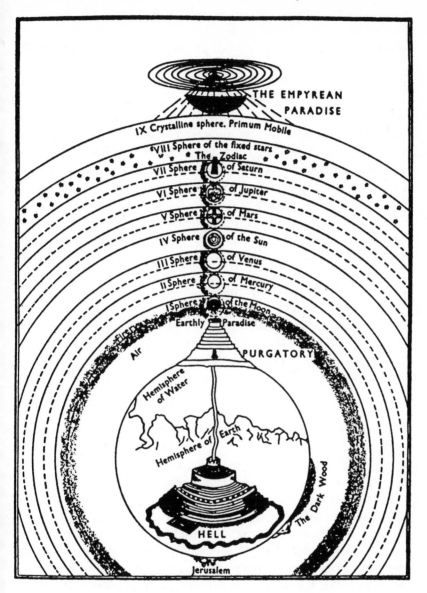

Figure 2.4: The View of the Universe presented by the Italian poet Dante Alighieri (1265–1321) in his book *The Divine Comedy*.

in motion by God through the angels who moved the various spheres. The planets, through their movement, exerted an influence on all physical things on earth and were thus instruments used by God to bring about material events. It was for the benefit of man, the crown of creation, that God continually guided the world.

While the *structure* of the medieval cosmos owed much to Greek thought, the account of its *origin* was based upon the Bible. Throughout the Middle Ages innumerable commentaries were written on the six creation days. As to the date of creation, the virtually unanimous opinion – based on the Genesis genealogies and other biblical chronological data – was that the world was created only a few thousand years before Christ.

The medieval conception of the universe achieved a harmonious unity between the concepts of God, the world, and man. The universe was seen to reflect both God's wisdom and his love: wisdom because everything displayed perfect order, love because it was an expression of his concern for man.

In short, the medieval universe was a perfectly ordered whole. It was static, hierarchical, and anthropocentric. Unfortunately, the harmony between cosmology and theology would also prove to be a weakness, for the demise of medieval cosmology led also, for many, to the downfall of the accompanying theology.

The Demise of Medieval Cosmology

This wondrous marriage between theology and science was to remain the dominant cosmology until the seventeenth century. A number of factors contributed to its ultimate collapse. Foremost among these was the trend in the new science to place great weight upon direct observation, rather than relying on the authority of the ancients. Consequently, it became increasingly evident, particularly in the sixteenth century, that Aristotelian physics and Ptolemaic astronomy were deficient.

Thus, for example, serious damage was caused by two events recorded by the Danish astronomer Tycho Brahe (1546–1601). On 11 November 1572 he observed a new star (that is, a 'nova'). This contradicted the basic doctrine that all change was confined to the sublunar, earthly sphere. Shortly thereafter, Tycho demonstrated that the great comet of 1577 was not a sub-lunary phenomena, as comets had until then been considered, but that it was moving through the planetary spheres. This shattered the belief in the immutability of the skies and the solidity of the celestial spheres.

The telescope, invented only a few years later, soon led to further difficulties. In 1610 Galileo showed that the surface of the moon was not perfect, as asserted by Aristotle, but had mountains and valleys similar to the earth. This suggested a similarity between earthly and heavenly matter. Later in the seventeenth century this likeness was further confirmed by Isaac Newton, who showed that the same physical laws applied to both. The development of Newtonian mechanics completed the overthrow of Aristotelian physics.

Galileo versus the Church

The most serious blow to medieval cosmology, however, was the removal of the earth from the centre of the universe. The notion of a heliocentric universe had already been entertained by the Greek astronomer Aristarchus of Samos (about 310–230 BC). Although it had never been very popular, this ancient idea was again taken up by Nicolas Copernicus (1473–1543), who hoped it might simplify the calculation of planetary positions (*Figure* 2.5). In this quest he did not quite succeed: the new system turned out to be no less complex than that of Ptolemy, requiring forty-eight epicycles, compared to the forty of Ptolemaic astronomy. Nevertheless, it did have the advantage of offering a simple explanation of certain peculiarities of the planetary motions, as well as allowing the calculation of the relative distances to the planets.

Nevertheless, it was still possible to devise equivalent models that retained the earth at the centre. For example, Tycho Brahe's model, where the planets encircled a sun rotating about a stationary earth, explained the planetary motions as well as did the heliocentric system (*Figure* 2.6).

The Copernican theory did not become widely accepted until the early 1600s, when it led to a famous episode in the history of science. Almost every book dealing with science and Christianity discusses the Roman Catholic Church's seventeenth-century condemnation of Italian scientist Galileo Galilei (1564–1642). Galileo promoted the Copernican theory that the earth was moving about a fixed sun; the Roman Catholic Church held this to be contrary to the Bible, which

NICOLAI COPERNICI

net,in quo terram cum orbe lunari tanquam epicyclo contineri
diximus . Quinto loco Venus nono menſe reducitur.¡Sextum
deniꝗ locum Mercurius tenet,octuaginta dierum ſpacio circū
currens,In medio uero omnium reſidet Sol. Quis enim in hoc

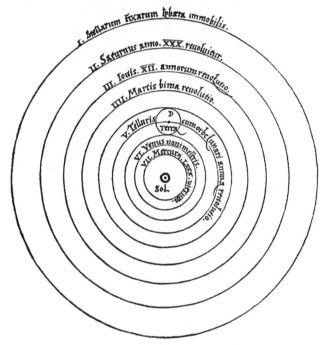

pulcherimo templo lampadem hanc in alio uel meliori loco po
neret,quàm unde totum ſimul poſsit illuminareꝰSiquidem non
inepte quidam lucernam mundi,alꞇ mentem, alꞇ rectorem uo=
cant. Trimegiſtus uiſibilem Deum,Sophoclis Electra intuentē
omnia.Ita profecto tanquam in ſolio re gali Sol reſidens circum
agentem gubernat Aſtrorum familiam. Tellus quoꝗ minime
fraudatur lunari miniſterio ,ſed ut Ariſtoteles de animalibus
ait,maximā Luna cū terra cognationē habet.Concipit interea à
Sole terra , & impregnatur annuo partu. Inuenimus igitur ſub
hac

Figure 2.5: The Heliocentric Universe according to Copernicus,
from his book *De Revolutionibus Orbium Coelestium* (1543).

spoke of a fixed earth. This resulted in much debate. Which was in absolute motion, the sun or the earth? Although politics, personality clashes, and Aristotelian physics all played major roles, the prime objection raised against the Copernican universe was that it clashed with the traditional reading of the Bible.

The principal difficulty was that none of the proofs presented in favour of the Copernican model was conclusive. The formidable Roman Catholic theologian, Cardinal Robert Bellarmine, Consultor of the Holy Office and a leader in the 1616 trial of Galileo, remarked in a letter to Galileo:

> If there were a real proof . . . that the Sun does not go around the Earth but the Earth around the Sun, then we would have to proceed with great circumspection in explaining those passages of Scripture which appear to teach the contrary, and we should rather have to say that we did not understand them than declare an opinion false which is proved to be true. But I do not think there is any such proof since none has been shown to me. To demonstrate that the appearances are saved by assuming the sun at the centre and the earth in the heavens is not the same thing as to demonstrate that in fact the sun is in the centre . . . I believe that the first demonstration may exist, but I have grave doubts about the second; and in case of doubt one may not abandon the Holy Scriptures as expounded by the holy Fathers.[1]

Bellarmine had no difficulty accepting the Copernican model as a useful hypothesis. But he objected to its elevation as a truth: to do that would require definite proofs, proofs that Galileo could not supply. Galileo did present a certain amount of evidence, consisting primarily of observations made with the recently invented telescope. This included such novelties as the satellites of Jupiter, the phases of Venus, craters on the Moon, and numerous new stars. Nevertheless, while these were all consistent with the Copernican model, none provided direct evidence for it. All of these observations could still be accommodated within a geocentric model.

On 5 March 1616 the General Congregation of the Index ruled that the doctrine of the motion of the earth and the immobility of the sun was 'false and altogether opposed to Scripture'.[2]

---

[1] Quoted in Arthur Koestler, *The Sleepwalkers*, Harmondsworth: Penguin Books, 1968, p. 454.   [2] *Ibid.*, p. 462.

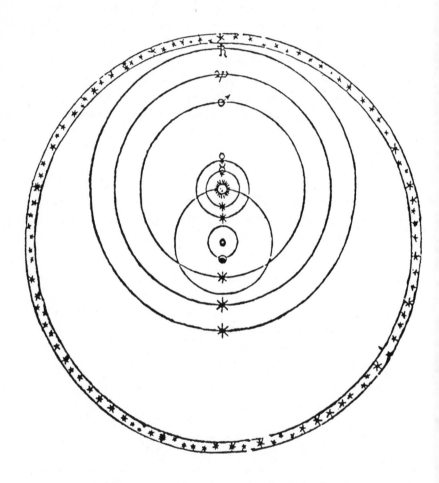

Figure 2.6: The System of Tycho Brahe, from his book *De Mundi Aetherei Recentioribus Phaenomenis* (1588).

The church's treatment of Galileo has caused endless embarrassment to Christians. After enduring centuries of ridicule, the Roman Church, in October 1992, finally reversed its judgment on Galileo.

Had the Roman Church erred in its condemnation of Galileo? The matter is not quite as clear-cut as most people take it to be. Indeed, the question of absolute motion can hardly be answered on scientific grounds. Of course, it is clear that the earth and the stars are moving with respect to each other. But this could be explained in different ways. We could take the earth as moving with respect to the fixed stars. Or we could take the stars as moving with respect to a fixed earth. Or we could take both to be in motion with respect to some other fixed point. Observationally these are all equivalent since all we can ever observe is *relative* motion, not *absolute* motion. To make the claim that it is 'really' the earth, rather than the rest of the physical universe, that is moving is to go beyond the observational evidence. Moreover, upon deeper reflection, what can it possibly mean to say that, for example, the distant stars are at rest? At rest with respect to what? The implication is that there exists some other feature of the universe with respect to which the motion of the stars can be measured. This in turn raises the further question as to whether this new feature is 'at rest' and with respect to what. And so on.

To see whether the earth is 'really' moving we must step outside the physical universe on to a fixed resting point. This only God can do. Hence, ultimately, it is only God who can adequately answer the question of absolute motion.

In short, the question as to whether it is really the earth or the sun that moves cannot be answered through scientific investigation. There are no direct proofs of the earth's motion; there cannot be. At its deepest level the question is not even scientifically meaningful. The definition of what constitutes an 'absolute' standard depends largely on non-observational, philosophical considerations.

This limitation of scientific knowledge has been stressed by many great scientists and philosophers. It is nowadays generally granted by scientists that the question of absolute motion is not a scientific one. To quote the famous British philosopher Bertrand Russell:

> Before Copernicus, people thought that the earth stood still and that the heavens revolved about it once a day. Copernicus taught that 'really' the earth revolves once a day, and the daily rotation of sun and stars is

only 'apparent' . . . But in the modern theory the question between Copernicus and his predecessors is merely one of convenience; all motion is relative, and there is no difference between the two . . . Astronomy is easier if we take the sun as fixed than if we take the earth . . . But to say more for Copernicus is to assume absolute motion, which is a fiction. It is a mere convention to take one body as at rest. All such conventions are equally legitimate, though not all are equally convenient.[1]

In a recent article[2] it has been shown that, in a closed universe, general relativity predicts the same effects, regardless of whether we take the earth to be rotating in a fixed universe or whether we take the universe to be revolving about a fixed earth: only relative motion is physically important.

It is amusing to note that in scientific circles there has been some discomfort over Galileo's stance. After the Vatican's recent rehabilitation of Galileo, an editorial in *Nature*, a prominent British science magazine (5 November 1992, p. 2), admonished the Vatican for doing it so belatedly and grudgingly. But then the editor went on to wonder whether the earth goes about the sun in any but a relative sense, adding 'Galileo was probably too good a scientist to commit himself to an absolute view'. Here the *Nature* editor is wrong: it was precisely Galileo's insistence on an absolute view of the earth's motion that got him into trouble.

Theological Consequences

The crucial issue in the Galileo case was that of epistemology. In particular, the debate raged over the nature and extent of biblical authority, as well as over the status of scientific theories. As we already noted, Galileo presented the Copernican system not as a mere theory, but as the truth, a truth before which Scripture, or at least the Church's interpretation of it, had to retreat. He advocated a realist view of scientific theories, as opposed to the more moderate claims of Bellarmine's instrumentalist suggestion.

[1] *The ABC of Relativity*, London: Allen and Unwin, 1958, p. 13.
[2] D. Lynden-Bell, J. Katz and J. Bicak, 'Mach's Principle from the Relativistic Constraint Equations', *Monthly Notices of the Royal Astronomical Society*, 1995, 272, pp. 150–60.

Galileo discussed his views on the relationship between science and Scripture in his *Letter to the Grand Duchess Christina* (1615). There he argued that certain passages in Scripture should not be taken literally, one reason being that:

> These propositions uttered by the Holy Ghost were set down by the sacred scribes in order to accommodate them to the capacities of the common people, who are rude and unlearned.[1]

A second reason he gave[2] was that cosmology is irrelevant to the central purpose of the Bible, which is to teach us how to attain salvation: 'Scripture tells us how to go to heaven, not how the heavens go'. Also, Galileo stated:

> I think that in discussions of physical problems we ought to begin not from the authority of scriptural passages, but from sense experiences and necessary demonstrations . . . nothing physical which sense experience sets before our eyes, or which necessary demonstrations prove to us, ought to be called into question (much less condemned) upon the testimony of biblical passages which may have some different meaning beneath their words. We must take heed, in handling the doctrine of Moses, that we altogether avoid saying . . . anything which contradicts manifest experience and reasoning of philosophy or the other sciences. For since every truth is in agreement with all other truth, the truth of Holy Writ cannot be contrary to the solid reasons and experiences of human knowledge.[3]

For Christians the drama of salvation had always been central, and therefore more important than nature. Now Galileo not only considered the Book of Nature to be as significant as the Book of Scripture, but he assumed that the Book of Nature also spoke more clearly than the Book of Scripture. With Galileo, the scientific enquiry of nature acquired an independent status to which other truths had to conform. Galileo's attitude has been described as a threat to Christian understanding:

> A tradition was forged in which the increasing clarity discerned through nature was set against the prevailing unclarity of Scripture, with the

---

[1] *Letter to the Grand Duchess Christina* (1615) in *Discoveries and Opinions of Galileo*, translated by Stillman Drake, New York: Doubleday Anchor, 1957, p. 182.
[2] *Ibid.*, p. 188.   [3] *Ibid.*, pp. 182–6.

attendant hope that thereby the latter might be purged of its obscurity. In retrospect, it is clear that this can only be accomplished by a logic which no longer took its cue from the biblical revelation but from a philosophy which determined the content from its own angle of vision. In Galileo, an independent natural basis for religion had begun to determine the biblical understanding of revelation. Of this Galileo was certainly unaware.[1]

Whether Galileo was aware of it or not, his position was grounded upon an epistemology that led to a slow but steady reduction in biblical authority.

Many others who accepted the new astronomy also accepted Galileo's view of the relationship between the two Books. The prominent German astronomer Johannes Kepler (1571–1630), who also was much concerned with reconciling science and Scripture, was prepared to re-interpret Scripture in a flexible manner through the widely-held notion of accommodation.

This position was opposed by a number of theologians who insisted on the primacy of Scripture even in astronomical matters. For example, the Lutheran Abraham Calovius declared, in the middle of the seventeenth century, that in natural matters Copernicus was not to have more authority than the Word of God. He feared that the acceptance of the notion that biblical passages had been accommodated to common ways of thinking would be like opening a hole in the dyke which would eventually destroy the dyke itself. Hence Calovius held that no error, even in unimportant matters, could have any place in Scripture. This affirmation of inerrancy even in scientific matters was echoed by many others, including such eminent Reformed theologians as Gisbert Voet (1588–1676) and Francis Turretin (1623–87). Turretin considered the admission of any error, however small, to be a repudiation of the authority of Scripture. Thus, on scriptural grounds, these men rejected Copernicus. They sensed that to capitulate at any point would demand capitulation all along the line.

Many intellectuals were not content to look for other interpretations of Scripture. They considered that science had proven the geocentric viewpoint of the Bible false. This led to their rejection of

---

[1] John Dillenberger, *Protestant Thought and Natural Science*, New York: Abingdon Press, 1960, p. 90.

the inerrancy of the Bible and, eventually, to the rejection of all revealed religion. Deism, which rejected every form of revealed religion as incompatible with science and attempted to construct a natural theology, became an important movement in the eighteenth century. God was seen primarily as the architect of the universe, leaving it to run by itself in accordance with the laws he had imposed on nature. Atheism, which also came into prominence in the eighteenth century, went even further by explicitly rejecting any concept of God.

The triumph of Copernicanism has had far-reaching effects on the Christian community. By accepting the new astronomy Christians gave tacit approval to the underlying secular epistemology of Galileo and his supporters. In permitting a scientific theory to dictate the interpretation of Scripture they abandoned the epistemological supremacy of Scripture. Human reason came to be considered as an independent source of truth, a source superior to Scripture – at least in scientific matters.

Pre-Modern Cosmology

The cosmological model of Copernicus was still bounded by the outer sphere of fixed stars, which was now centred on the sun rather than on the earth. However, since the apparent motion of the outer sphere was now attributed to the motion of the earth, the stellar sphere could be considered to be at rest. The removal of the motion of the stellar sphere swept away the prime argument for its finite size. Thus, as a natural consequence of Copernican cosmology, an infinite universe could now be contemplated.

This step, not made by Copernicus himself, was taken in 1576 by Thomas Digges (1543–95), an English astronomer and early convert to Copernicanism. He took away the outer edge of the universe, placing heaven with its celestial beings within an infinite space of stars (*Figure* 2.7).

Newtonian Cosmology

The new cosmology that replaced the old owed much to the great English scientist Sir Isaac Newton (1642–1727). Through his theories of gravity and motion, the universe came to be seen as a huge machine governed by mathematical equations. Yet this clockwork mechanism, created by God, did not quite run by itself. Newton

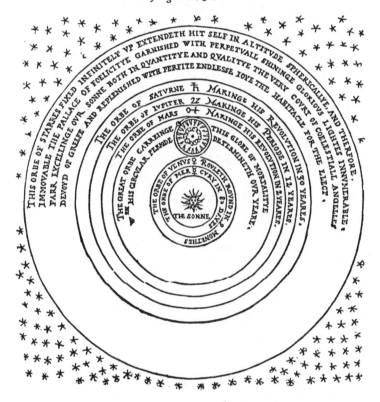

Figure 2.7: The Heliocentric Universe of Thomas Digges, from his *A Perfit Description of the Caelestial Orbes* (1576).

found that his mechanics could not account for the apparent stability of the solar system. He proposed that God interfered from time to time to keep the planetary motions on track. Indeed, Newton saw this mechanical deficiency as a proof for the existence of God. This extraordinary dependency on God was removed in the next century by the Frenchman Pierre-Simon Laplace (1749–1827), who was able to show that Newtonian mechanics itself sufficed to keep the solar system stable: no supernatural intervention was required.

According to Newton, time and space have always existed. The material universe was created a finite time ago in an infinite empty space. Newton considered the material world to be of finite size, surrounded by an infinite empty space. His followers, however, soon let the material universe fill all of infinite space, since they saw no reason to limit God's creative activity to just a small portion of space. Similar reasoning led to the removal of restrictions on God's creative action in time. The created world became infinite in both space and time.

Since an infinite and eternal world has no need of creation, God soon became superfluous as a Creator. Moreover, while Newton had considered space to be an attribute of God, embodying his presence and action, the new philosophy gradually came to look upon space more as the void of the ancient Greek atomists. Space was emptied of everything – including God.[1] In spite of Newton's aim to bolster a theistic concept of the universe, the cosmos that emerged from Newtonian mechanics had no need for God.

Thus the movement initiated by Copernicus and carried on by Kepler, Galileo, and Newton promoted an increasingly mechanistic view of the universe. God was gradually removed as an active force in the physical world. Kuhn summarizes this trend as follows:

> In the clockwork universe God frequently appeared to be only the clockmaker, the Being who had shaped the atomic parts, established the laws of their motion, and then left them to run themselves. Deism, an elaborated version of this view, was an important ingredient in late 17th and 18th century thought. As it advanced, the belief in miracles declined, for miracles were a suspension of mechanical law and a direct intervention by God and his angels in terrestrial affairs. By the end of

[1] Alexandre Koyré, *From the Closed World to the Infinite Universe*, Baltimore: John Hopkins Press, 1957, pp. 274–6.

the 18th century an increasing number of men, scientists and non-scientists alike, saw no need to posit the existence of God.[1]

Not only did the medieval world-view allow for the direct interaction of God with his creation, it also had a special place for God: the throne of God was located in the heavenly Empyrean, which lay beyond the finite sphere of the fixed stars. Up to the time of Newton, Christians had generally considered heaven to be a physical place located beyond the stars. This was all changed as a result of the Copernican revolution. When the closed universe was replaced with an infinite space, there was no longer any place for heaven. Although, as we saw, Thomas Digges still mingled his stellar and theological heavens, God was gradually expelled from this heaven, leaving only the stars. Thus man was left alone, lost in an infinite maze.

The Dynamic Universe

Initially the Newtonian universe was essentially static: it did not change significantly over time. This conception did not last long. By the eighteenth century, the notion of change over time became popular in various disciplines, particularly geology and biology. Increasing interest was shown in the question of origins. In cosmology new theories were proposed to account for the formation of the celestial objects.

The infinite Newtonian universe had abandoned both geocentricity and heliocentricity. Infinite space was at first thought to be uniformly populated with stars similar to the sun. It soon became evident, however, that the stars were not randomly scattered through space. Rather, most appeared to be grouped together in the Milky Way. Thomas Wright (1711–86) speculated in 1750 that the Milky Way consisted of either a sphere or a disk of stars circling about the centre. The centre was a supernatural source from whence originated all the laws of nature. By this time a number of faint and fuzzy objects had been observed. Wright conjectured that these distant clouds or 'nebulae' were in fact collections of stars similar to the Milky Way. According to him the universe was filled with infinitely many centres of creation.

[1] T. S. Kuhn, *The Copernican Revolution*, Cambridge, Mass.: Harvard University Press, 1957, p. 233..

Shortly thereafter, in 1755, the German philosopher Immanuel Kant (1724–1804) went a step further and proposed a naturalistic origin for all celestial bodies in the universe. He suggested that initially the universe consisted of an infinite, nearly uniform gas. Due to gravitational attraction, collections of matter were formed. Their random motions gave the condensing clumps of matter a small spin. As the systems contracted further their spins increased and galaxies were formed. Inside the galaxies a similar process formed individual stars and planets. This 'nebular hypothesis' for the origin of the universe was further expounded by Laplace. The main point of contention concerned the interpretation of the faint nebulae. Laplace thought they were merely clouds of gas associated with the Milky Way. His universe was centred upon a single gigantic Milky Way surrounded by circling clouds of gas. The opposing view of Wright and Kant was that of an infinity of 'island universes' like the Milky Way. This debate was finally resolved in the 1920s, when new observations vindicated the multi-galaxy position.

The notion of a dynamic, evolving universe became extremely popular in the latter half of the nineteenth century, particularly with the development of biological evolution. The writings of Charles Darwin (1809–82) were particularly influential. His principal work, *On the Origin of Species* (1859) dealt mainly with the evolution of plants and animals. In his *Descent of Man* (1871) he extended the principle of evolution to include also the origin of man. This idea was soon applied also to society, incorporating the attractive ideal of human progress. Soon the evolutionary model of the universe became the dominant worldview. From the start, there had been opposition from religious quarters, but most theologians managed to adapt their Christianity to the evolutionary cosmos.

Thus a naturalistic, scientific model finally claimed to account for the formation of the entire universe, with all its contents. The static, finite, geocentric and theistic clockwork mechanism of medieval man had been replaced by a dynamic, infinite, materialistic organism continually evolving upwards.

Heat Death

The establishment of the evolutionary cosmos initially generated an optimistic view of the future. The defenders of evolution felt that the universe was steadily improving. Darwin himself concluded:

> As natural selection works solely by and for the good of each being, all corporeal and mental endowments will tend to progress towards perfection.[1]

This optimistic spirit was soon to be severely jolted.

The challenge came from the new science of thermodynamics, the study of heat. The industrial revolution, which had gained momentum in the early nineteenth century, was strongly dependent upon the development of efficient machinery. By 1850, studies of steam engines and other processes involving energy exchanges led to the discovery of two fundamental principles.

The first of these, the first law of thermodynamics, as it became known, had to do with the conservation of energy. This law postulates that, while energy can be transformed from one form to another, energy can never be created or destroyed. Consider, for example, a waterfall. As the water plunges downward, its gravitational potential energy, due to its height, is converted to mechanical energy. If this is used to drive a turbine, the energy can in turn be transformed to electric energy. Were this power to be used to operate a pump, we could pump the water back to its original height. The first law asserts that, if we could neglect energy loss due to friction, the waterfall generates just enough electrical power to enable all the water to be pumped back up. No new additional energy can be generated.

If we take friction into account, as we must in practice, the situation worsens. This brings us to the second law of thermodynamics, which deals with the amount of *useful* energy available. It was first formulated in 1851 by Rudolph Clausius (1822–88) at Berlin and William Thomson (Lord Kelvin, 1824–1907) in Glasgow. The second law specifies that, in any actual physical process, useful energy is always lost; frictional effects will always cause some of the available energy to be dissipated as heat. If we drop a ball onto a flat, steady floor, we find that it will never quite bounce back to its initial position. Some mechanical energy is always lost, transformed into heating either the ball or its surroundings.

[1] Darwin, *On the Origin of the Species,* 2nd ed., 1859, London: John Murray, p. 486.

The First Law states that in any process the final energy output cannot exceed the energy input. The Second Law stipulates that we cannot even break even: the usable energy generated by a machine is always less than the energy input. This rules out the possibility of a perpetual motion machine. It is commonly believed that the Second Law of Thermodynamics is one of the most basic laws of all science.

Clausius defined the 'entropy' of a system as a measure of the state of disorder, or randomness, of the system. The higher the degree of disorder, the higher the entropy. Consider, for example, a room full of air molecules. If the air molecules all happen to be in one half of the room (a most unlikely event!) this corresponds to a highly ordered state, having a very low entropy. If the air molecules are mixed throughout the room, the order is lost and the entropy is now high. According to Clausius, all systems tend to develop toward a state of 'equilibrium', where there is no net flow of energy. Systems tend to go from an ordered state to a disordered state, rather than vice-versa. Thus, left to itself, a sand castle will degenerate into a pile of sand, whereas the reverse does not happen. Real processes tend to be irreversible.

Applying this principle to the universe as a whole, Clausius concluded that the total energy in the universe is constant and its entropy tends towards a maximum. A similar conclusion was also reached by the German physicist Hermann von Helmholtz in 1854. He deduced some far-reaching consequences. If the universe is continually running down into a state of disorder, then it must have been 'wound up' some finite time in the past by some process violating the second law. Furthermore, at some finite time in the future the universe will become totally disordered. It will tend toward an equilibrium state where each region has the same temperature. At that time the universe will have no more useful energy left and life in any form must disappear. This has been called the 'heat death' of the universe.

The new thermodynamic laws put fundamental restrictions on cosmological theorizing. The Second Law, in particular, with its gloomy predictions of the future demise of life in the universe, snuffed out the optimistic view of the universe evolving to ever greater perfection. In its place came a sense of despair, a feeling that our habitable universe was a mere statistical accident, with no future prospects and no ultimate purpose.

3

Modern Cosmology

In this chapter we shall examine theories of modern cosmology. Since big-bang cosmology is by far the most popular cosmology, it will be the prime focus of our discussion. We shall review its history and observational support, assess its strengths and weaknesses, and briefly consider a variety of alternatives. In the latter part of the chapter we shall discuss a number of basic cosmological assumptions that are commonly made, as well as the difficulty of verifying these.

A Brief History of the Big Bang

Edgar Allan Poe, better known for his short stories, was the first to suggest that the universe originated in a gigantic explosion. In his small book *Eureka*, published in 1848, Poe describes how the universe was created by God, out of nothing, as an exploding primordial particle. Initially, matter shot out in all directions. As the universe expanded, gravity gradually caused the atoms to condense into stars and planets. Eventually, sometime in the distant future, gravity will halt the expansion and a contraction will set in. The cosmos will finally return to its initial state, a tiny point, at which time it will disappear.

Poe did not believe our universe could be infinite. He referred to *Olbers' Paradox*, an objection to an infinite universe raised by Heinrich Olbers in 1823 and others before him. According to Olbers, if there were an infinite number of stars, then if we looked in any direction we should eventually end up at a star. The night sky should

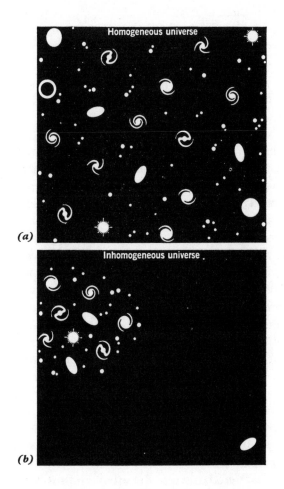

Figure 3.1: Distribution of Matter in the Universe.
  (a) Homogeneous universe. Matter is spread out uniformly over
    large distances.
  (b) Inhomogeneous universe. Matter is not uniformly distributed
    over large distances.
(From Michael Zeilik, *Conceptual Astronomy*, New York: John Wiley &
Son Inc., 1992.)

therefore be uniformly bright with starlight. Since this is not the case, Olbers concluded that our universe is finite.

However, Poe did manage to retain an infinite, eternal universe. He speculated that there is an infinity of universes, each with its own god. But these universes are so immensely far from each other that there can be no communication among them. Furthermore, after our universe has collapsed God will generate a new universe, another pulse in an eternal cycle. Poe's model did not attract many scientists. Most continued to believe in some form of infinite, dynamically static, Newtonian universe.

Modern cosmology really began in 1917, when Albert Einstein first applied his new gravitational theory – known as *general relativity* – to the universe as a whole. Einstein assumed that the universe was *homogeneous*, which means that, on a large scale, matter was spread uniformly throughout the universe (see *Figure* 3.1). He also applied the *cosmological principle*, which assumed that any particular region looked much the same as any other. The cosmological principle implies that the universe has no edges since, if there were an edge, an observer near the edge would have a special vantage point.

Until then the only way to avoid edges was to have an infinite universe. Another possibility was now offered by relativity: the *curvature* of space. Einstein's theory postulated that the gravitational effect of matter would cause space to be *curved*. If there was enough matter the resultant gravitational field would be strong enough to cause space to curve in on itself, thus creating a finite universe with no edges. Such a finite, yet unbounded, universe is called a *closed* universe. A less dense universe that is not closed is considered to be *open*. In an open universe the cosmological principle can hold only if the universe is infinite in size. The different geometries of space are compared in *Figure* 3.2

To visualize a closed universe directly is impossible, as it really involves four-dimensional geometry. But one could consider a two-dimensional analogy. Consider a small piece of wire. If it is straight it will have two ends or 'edges', but if we bend it into a circle then we have a finite length with no 'edges'. Or we could consider the surface of a ball to be a finite two-dimensional surface, with no edges, embedded within a three-dimensional space. In a similar fashion our three-dimensional universe could be imagined to be a finite volume,

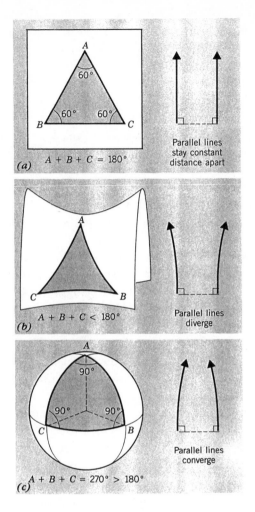

Figure 3.2: Comparison of Space Geometries.

(a) Flat geometry. The sum of the angles of a triangle is always 180 degrees.

(b) Hyperbolic (open) geometry. The sum of the angles of a triangle is always less than 180 degrees.

(c) Spherical (closed) geometry. The sum of the angles of a triangle is always greater than 180 degrees.

(From Michael Zeilik, *Conceptual Astronomy*, New York: John Wiley & Sons Inc., 1992.)

with no edges, embedded within a higher-dimensional space. With relativity, it was possible to return to a finite universe and still hold on to the cosmological principle of uniformity.

There was one difficulty, however. Einstein felt that the universe should be static, remaining essentially the same over a period of time. Since the gravitational field of a finite universe would cause it to collapse, Einstein added a repulsive force to his cosmological model to prevent such an inward motion. This term, called 'the cosmological constant', or 'Lambda', would counterbalance the attractive force of gravity. The force was postulated to increase with distance so that its local contribution would be too small to be detected. Only on a cosmological scale, when the contribution from the most distant galaxies became significant, would this force become important.

Shortly afterwards, in the 1920s, it was discovered that the light from distant galaxies was shifted towards the red. This was taken as evidence that the galaxies, rather than being stationary, were moving outwards, away from the earth. On the basis of this new development, the big-bang theory was resurrected in modern form by the Belgian cosmologist and priest, Georges-Henri Lemaître, in the late 1920s. Lemaître hypothesized that the universe originally started off as an explosion of the 'primeval atom', an initially very dense concentration of matter.

As proof of the primeval explosion Lemaître pointed to cosmic rays (high-energy particles that bombard the earth from space). Lemaître argued that no known astronomical source could have produced these and hence they must have been caused by the unusual conditions of the big-bang explosion. Another factor apparently supporting this was the distribution of the cosmic rays: they seemed to come uniformly from every direction, as might be expected if they arose from the big bang. It was thought that they could not have come from galaxies, since these are irregularly distributed.

However, in the next decades it was shown that cosmic rays could be generated by electromagnetic forces now operating in interstellar space. Moreover, it became apparent that most cosmic rays came from our own galaxy, their uniform distribution being due to the curving of their paths by the galaxy's magnetic field. Instead of coming from the distant ends of the universe, reflecting the birthpangs of the cosmos, cosmic rays turned out to be a very local phenomenon. Plagued by a number of observational and theoretical shortcomings, Lemaître's big-bang cosmology found very few supporters.

The big-bang theory was revived by George Gamow in 1946. Gamow conjectured that, if the big bang was a huge nuclear explosion, its extremely high density and temperature could generate the observed proportions of hydrogen, helium, and other elements in the universe. Within months, however, Fred Hoyle showed that nuclear processes in stars were sufficient to produce the heavy elements in approximately the right abundances, although some other mechanism was needed to produce the observed amount of helium.

In 1948 Hoyle, along with Herman Bondi and Thomas Gold, formulated an alternative cosmology, the steady-state model. This theory was based on what has been called the *perfect cosmological principle*, which asserts that the universe looks roughly the same, not only at all places, but also at all times. The rate of expansion, the space density and age distribution of the galaxies are all assumed to be constant. Since the expansion will tend to spread out the galaxies, the theory demands that new matter be continuously created – out of nothing – at precisely the right rate to keep the density constant. New galaxies are then formed from the newly created matter as the old galaxies are thinned out by expansion.

One of the main motivations for this cosmology was to avoid what Hoyle considered to be theistic implications of the initial singularity. Yet, while this model avoids the creation *ex nihilo* allegedly implied by the big bang, its own concept of continuous creation indicates not just one act of creation *ex nihilo*, but an infinite number of them.

A major breakthrough for the big bang came in 1965. Gamow had deduced that the initial fireball should have left behind radiation in the form of radio waves. His calculations predicted that this radiation should by now have cooled to a temperature of about 30 degrees Kelvin (zero degrees Kelvin corresponds to absolute zero, the lowest possible temperature, which is at -273 degrees Centigrade). Also, the radiation was to be *isotropic*, that is, uniformly distributed in all directions. In 1965 such radiation was actually observed, although at only 3 degrees Kelvin.

Although steady-state cosmology had enjoyed some popularity for a few decades, particularly among British cosmologists, the 1965 discovery of the background radiation caused most cosmologists to favour the big-bang theory. Whereas this radiation, at least its main features, arises naturally in the big-bang model, the steady-state model had a more difficult time explaining it, though several possible explanations were constructed.

According to the modern 'standard big-bang model', the universe originated about 10 to 15 billion years ago in an explosion of energy originating from a tiny point, a 'singularity'. It started off very hot, very dense, and in a state of very rapid expansion. As the universe expanded it cooled. Within the first few minutes, the initial matter (mainly sub-atomic particles) condensed into hydrogen, helium, and small traces of other light elements. As time went on, clumps of matter contracted, due to gravity, to form galaxies. Inside the galaxies, smaller clumps contracted to form stars. As the stars contracted gravitational energy was converted into heat. Eventually the temperatures inside the stars became high enough to generate nuclear reactions, from which carbon, oxygen, and other heavy elements were formed. Later, as stars evolved, they ejected matter into interstellar space. From this interstellar matter, second-generation stars, now containing higher amounts of heavier elements than the first batch, were formed. Some of these stars had planets. On at least one planet (that is, the Earth) random interactions of molecules produced a primitive form of life. Eventually more complicated plants and animals evolved, culminating in the appearance of man.

Thus far the creation story according to big-bang cosmology. It is a very comprehensive theory that strives to explain all of physical reality in terms of a dynamic evolving universe that can be traced back to the initial singularity.

Explaining the Observations

How well founded is the big-bang model? As we have already noted, the big-bang theory rests on three pillars of observational evidence: galactic red shifts, elemental abundances, and background radiation. To move from these observational facts to their interpretation as velocities and residues of an initial big-bang explosion involves a big jump that warrants a closer examination.

1. Red Shifts

In the late 1920s the American astronomer Edwin Hubble discovered that light from galaxies was shifted towards the red, low-frequency end of the spectrum. A similar lowering of pitch can be noted when, for example, a police siren moves past us. As the siren moves away the sound waves it emits are stretched by the motion of the siren itself, causing us to hear the noise at a lower frequency. This is called the Doppler effect. Hence, a simple explanation of the galactic redshifts is that the galaxies are receding from us.

Hubble found that the red shift was roughly proportional to the distance to the galaxy. This relationship, which became known as Hubble's law, was interpreted by many astronomers as evidence the universe as a whole is expanding.

It should be noted that, in big-bang cosmology, the red shift is postulated to be caused, not by galaxies moving *through space*, but by an expansion of *space itself*. As space expands the wavelength of light is likewise stretched, corresponding to a reduction in its frequency. The red shift is calculated by subtracting the original, emitted wavelength from the observed, received wavelength, and then dividing by the emitted wavelength. This red shift number is denoted by the symbol z. For example, a red shift of $z=1$ indicates a doubling of wavelength since emission and, hence, implies that the emission event occurred when the universe was half its current size.

There are, however, some difficulties with this velocity interpretation of the red shift. The astronomer Halton Arp[1] has observed many pairs of galaxies that seem to be very close to each other, even physically connected, yet have greatly differing red shifts. This suggests that at least some of the red shifts have a cause other than motion. However, if some of the red shifts have a non-motion cause, it is quite possible that most have such a cause, leaving us with a roughly static universe.

Further, Arp notes that red shifts tend to cluster about preferred z values such as 0.06, 0.3, 0.6, 0.9, 1.4, and 1.96. Extensive evidence for red shift periodicity and variability has been found by Tifft[2]. This is contrary to what is expected in a homogeneous, expanding universe

---

[1] *Seeing Red*, Montreal: Apeiron, 1998.
[2] W. G. Tifft, 'Global Redshift Periodicities and Periodicity Variability', *Astrophysical Journal*, 1997, 485, pp. 465–83.

and indicates either that we are at the centre of a series of expanding shells or that the red shifts have some other, non-velocity, cause.

There are further difficulties. Hubble's red-shift-distance relation, the major pillar supporting big-bang cosmology, was initially based on an analysis of only a few dozen galaxies. Newer, much more complete, statistical analyses of thousands of galaxies, however, depart significantly from Hubble's linear law. Studies by I. E. Segal[1,2] find that a quadratic relation, where the red shift varies as the square of the distance, gives a much better fit. This contradicts big-bang expansion but accords well with Segal's chronometric cosmology, a static cosmology wherein the red shift is directly proportional to space curvature.[3]

Since a red shift of light corresponds to a lowering of its frequency, and since the energy of light is proportional to its frequency, a red shift implies a loss of energy. One problem in the big-bang model is how to account for the energy lost by the red-shifted light. It seems just to disappear, implying non-conservation of energy. The prominent Princeton cosmologist P. J. E. Peebles asks:

> Where does the lost energy go? . . . The resolution of this paradox is that while energy conservation is a good local concept . . . there is not a general global energy conservation law in general relativity theory.[4]

Earlier, a similar conclusion was reached by Edward Harrison, who, in his classic book *Cosmology*, wrote:

> The conclusion, whether we like it or not, is obvious: Energy in the universe is not conserved. The conservation-of-energy principle serves us well in all sciences except cosmology.[5]

---

[1] I. E. Segal, J. F. Nicoll, P. Wu, Z. Zhou, 'Statistically Efficient Testing of the Hubble and Lundmark Laws on IRAS Galaxy Samples', *Astrophysical Journal,* 1993, *411*, pp. 465–84.

[2] I. E. Segal, J. F. Nicoll, 'Statistics of a Complete High-Redshift Quasar Survey and Predictions of Nonevolutionary Cosmologies', *Astrophysical Journal,* 1996, *459*, p. 496.

[3] I. E. Segal and Z. Zhou, 'Maxwell's Equations in the Einstein Universe and Chronometric Cosmology', *Astrophysical Journal Supplement,* 1995, *100*, p. 307.

[4] *Principles of Physical Cosmology,* Princeton: The University Press, 1993, p. 138.

[5] E. R. Harrison, *Cosmology: The Science of the Universe*, Cambridge: The University Press, 1981, p. 277.

Such an inexplicable breaking of one of the most fundamental concepts in science is not very satisfactory. Could the red shift have some other, non-velocity cause? A host of alternative explanations of the red shifts have been proposed. The energy loss of light is usually postulated to be caused either by movement through a resisting medium, referred to as 'tired light', or by climbing out of a strong gravitational field, referred to as a 'gravitational red shift'. Numerous static-universe cosmologies, based on non-velocity views of the red shift, have been devised.

a. Tired Light

The motion interpretation of the redshifts was questioned almost from the start. Already in 1929 the astronomer Fritz Zwicky proposed that the redshift was caused by energy loss of light during its journey through space. One advantage of tired-light theories is that they naturally predict a redshift proportional to the distance travelled, in accordance with Hubble's law. Hubble himself, throughout his life, strongly favoured the tired-light theory over the expansion view, but he could offer no plausible physical mechanism generating such an effect. The trick is for the units of light, photons, to lose energy without significant scattering, else the galactic images should be fuzzier than they actually are.

More recently, the tired-light theory has been promoted by a number of astronomers. Ghosh[1] lists twenty non-velocity red-shift mechanisms. In tired-light theories for the red shift, it is generally postulated that the energy lost by the light is re-radiated as low-temperature energy, thereby accounting also for the microwave background radiation.

Paul La Violette, after performing a variety of tests on the two alternative red-shift explanations, concluded that the tired-light theory fits the observations much better than does the expanding universe model.[2]

---

[1] A. Ghosh, 'Velocity-dependent Inertial Induction: a Possible Tired-Light Mechanism', *Apeiron*, 1991, 9-10, pp. 35–44. For other possible mechanisms, see the papers by Kierein, Marmet and Reber, D. F. Crawford, Fischer and Van Flandern in the Bibliography.

[2] P. A. La Violette, *Beyond the Big Bang: Ancient Myth and the Science of Continuous Creation*, Rochester, Vermont: Park Street Press, 1995.

b. Gravitational Red Shift

G. F. R. Ellis has shown that the red-shifted galaxies and the microwave background radiation can be explained by a static, spherically-symmetric universe with two centres, our galaxy being near one of the centres.[1] The systematic red shifts of the galaxies are then interpreted as cosmological gravitational red shifts, while the background radiation originates from a hot gas surrounding a singularity situated at the second centre of the universe. While Ellis does not claim that the universe is like this model, he says that there exist no overwhelming arguments to show that such a model could not reproduce all the current observations. A somewhat similar static model, but having only one centre, has been developed by Rao and Annapurna.[2] Lately, another model, using both gravitational and Doppler red shifts, has been proposed by Robert Gentry.[3]

c. Changing Constants

Another static universe model has been constructed by the Russian V. S. Troitskii[4] who interprets the red shift as being due to a decrease in the speed of light. Such a mechanism would produce also the observed background radiation.

In 1931, Sir James Jeans advanced a model in which the size of atoms decreases in time. This would give the appearance of an expanding universe, although actually it is not expanding but everything in it, including us, is shrinking. This idea was later re-introduced by Hoyle[5] who claims that this model is indistinguishable from that of the expanding universe. The shrinkage can be understood if the masses of all the elementary particles increase, while the electric charge remains constant. In the past atoms would be bound more tightly about their nucleus, thus causing emitted radiation to be red-shifted. Arp[6], in a similar vein, proposes that the

---

[1] G. F. R. Ellis, 'Is the Universe Expanding?', *General Relativity and Gravitation*, 1978, 9, pp. 87–94.

[2] J. Krishna Rao, M. Annapurna, 'Spherically Symmetric Static Inhomogeneous Cosmological Models', *Pramana*, 1991, 36, pp. 95–103.

[3] Robert Gentry, 'A New Redshift Interpretation', *Modern Physics Letters A*, 1997, 12, p. 2919.

[4] V. S. Troitskii, 'Physical Constants and Evolution of the Universe', *Astrophysics and Space Science*, 1987, 139, pp. 389–411.

[5] Fred Hoyle, 'On the Origin of the Microwave Background', *Astrophysical Journal*, 1975, 196, p. 661.   [6] Arp, *Seeing Red*.

mass of elementary particles increases with age, speeding up the rate of atomic time, and resulting in a decreasing red shift with age.

Many of the alternative explanations for the red shift are rather speculative, and, like the motion interpretation, have serious problems of their own to overcome. Nevertheless, they illustrate that the red shifts can be interpreted within a variety of theoretical models and do not provide unambiguous support for big-bang cosmology.

2. Abundances of Elements

One way of testing big-bang cosmology is by its prediction of the relative abundances of the various elements in the universe. A 'hot' big bang, with very high temperatures in the initial dense state, would generate about 75% hydrogen, 25% helium-4, and much smaller amounts of deuterium, helium-3, lithium-7, lithium-6 and beryllium. Heavier elements are thought to be produced in subsequent stellar nuclear reactions, which could also alter the abundances of the lighter elements.

Observational measurements indicate that hydrogen does account for roughly three quarters of the total mass and helium about one quarter, with only traces of heavier elements.

However, the precise predictions of big-bang nucleosynthesis depends strongly on the ratio of photons to baryons (baryons are protons and neutrons, which form the bulk of normal matter) and the density of baryons, neither of which is known accurately. In practice, then, these are adjustable parameters which are set by matching the theoretical predictions with the observed abundances for one or two elements.

The difficulty is to subtract the effects of stellar elemental production from the observed densities, so that the initial abundances can be determined. Deuterium is fragile, easily destroyed in stars, and not produced in stars. Hence its presently observed abundance could be significantly less than the original amount. Ideally, one would like to measure the abundances of low-density gas at a very early phase (that is, with a high red shift) before it could become contaminated with stellar debris. Recently Burles[1] measured the deuterium abundance in high-red-shift ($z > 3$) hydrogen clouds, assumed to correspond to the

[1] Scott Burles *et al.*, 'Sharpening the Predictions of Big-Bang Nucleosynthesis', *Physical Review Letters*, 1999, *82*, pp. 4176–79.

primeval gas. From this he calculated the primeval baryon density and, from that, the predicted abundances of helium-4 and lithium-7. He found that the helium-4 value matches fairly closely with some observational determinations, but not with others, whereas the lithium-7 prediction is twice as much as that seen in old stars. Hence the model does not account for all the abundances of the light elements. Moreover, the baryon density determined by big-bang nucleosynthesis is much smaller than the density of matter as determined by dynamic considerations, such as the rotation of galaxies.

To save big-bang cosmology, it is postulated that most of the matter in the universe exists in the form of esoteric, non-baryonic matter, to be discussed in a later section.

A further difficulty is that many high-red-shift objects, which should reflect primordial conditions, have anomalous abundances. For example, a measure of the beryllium abundance in a metal-poor star, which should reflect the abundances of primordial matter, yielded a beryllium abundance about a thousand times greater than that predicted by big-bang cosmology.[1] Also, low-density regions at redshift $z = 3$ have been found to contain much higher concentrations of heavy elements than expected according to big-bang cosmology.[2]

Very remote quasars ('quasar' is short for 'quasi-stellar object', a star-like object emitting large amounts of energy at radio frequencies), whose red shift is thought to correspond to a time when the universe was less than a billion years old, have been found to contain more iron than the sun. Most iron is believed to come from supernovas in which one star in a binary explodes. But the binaries need at least a billion years to evolve to this stage.[3] How, then, could quasars have acquired so much iron within a billion years of the big bang?

In short, big-bang models have difficulty accounting for the observed abundances without resorting to special, artificially contrived, scenarios to account for the depletion of lithium, special local sources of beryllium and iron, and so on.

---

[1] G. Gilmore et al., 'First detection of beryllium in a very metal-poor star: a test of the standard Big Bang model', Astrophysical Journal, 1991, 378, pp. 17–21.

[2] J. Michael Shull, 'Intergalactic Pollution', Nature, 1999, 394, pp. 17–18.

[3] Jeff Hecht, 'Astronomers' Double Whammy Rocks Cosmology', New Scientist, 1994, 141, p. 16.

George Burbidge and Fred Hoyle have shown that the synthesis of cosmic helium from hydrogen in stars should have released almost exactly as much energy as that contained in the background radiation. They conclude that the helium was produced by hydrogen burning in stars rather than in the early stages of a big bang.[1] They also present evidence that the observed abundance of helium and the other light elements was generated in stellar processes. In a later paper Burbidge, Hoyle and Narlikar[2] give a brief description of their alternative, quasi-steady-state, cosmology.

Lerner[3] constructed scenarios wherein the observed abundances were formed through nucleosynthesis in cycles of stellar formation and explosion. Although deuterium and lithium are not produced by normal stars, they could be created through interactions of matter with cosmic rays. Van Flandern, too, asserts that his model can account for the observed abundances via an infinite cycle of star and galaxy formation, as modified by ongoing processes such as cosmic-ray effects.[4] Again, we note that alternative explanations for the observed elemental abundances involve at least as much fudging and special pleading as does big-bang cosmology. Here, too, the evidence does not unequivocally support any one such theory.

3. The Cosmic Microwave Background

The cosmic microwave background radiation (CMBR), first observed in 1965, provided further evidence for the big bang. According to the big-bang theory, CMBR photons last interacted with matter when the universe had cooled to a temperature of about 3000 Kelvin, around 300,000 years after the big bang. A map of the current CMBR is considered to give us a snapshot of the universe at that time. This radiation has since cooled to the 3-degree-Kelvin radiation

[1] 'The Origin of Helium and the Other Light Elements', *Astrophysical Journal*, 1998, *509*, pp. L1–L3.
[2] G. Burbidge, F. Hoyle and J. V. Narlikar, 'A Different Approach to Cosmology', *Physics Today*, 1999, 52 (April), pp. 38–44.
[3] E. J. Lerner, 'Plasma Models of Microwave Background and Primordial Elements: An Alternative to the Big Bang', *Laser and Particle Beams*, 1988, 6, pp. 456–68; 'Galactic Model of Element Formation', *IEEE Transactions on Plasma Science*, 1989, 17, pp. 259–63.
[4] Tom Van Flandern, *Dark Matter, Missing Planets and New Comets*, Berkeley: North Atlantic Books, 1993.

that is now detected. This is sometimes referred to as the big bang's 'afterglow' or 'smoking gun'. Its uniformity in all directions ('isotropy') is taken as strong evidence of the radiation's primeval origin.

Actually, the radiation is not quite uniform in all directions. There is a small departure from uniformity, corresponding to an apparent motion of the sun of 370 km/s with respect to the radiation. Taking into account the motion of the sun about the galaxy, this translates into a motion of 620 km/s for our local group of galaxies with respect to the CMBR.[1] Recent studies by Lauer and Postman[2] indicate that the 600 km/s velocity holds for all galaxies around us, out to at least 10% of the radius of the visible universe. This compares to a velocity variation of galaxies within local clusters of generally less than 100 km/s.

Such a large drift of the galaxies with respect to the background radiation is quite contrary to big-bang theory. The expansion of galaxies should have been much more uniform, with small local fluctuations, but, on the whole, at rest with respect to the CMBR.

What could account for the huge 600 km/s deviation? It has been conjectured that these galaxies are affected by the gravitational pull of a giant mass. But the observed deviation from uniform flow is so enormous that the scale of this perturber must be huge. No suitable object has been identified. Computer simulations of this data by Strauss[3] indicate that such phenomena are extremely improbable in any of the currently proposed big-bang models.

The assumption of homogeneity is further eroded by the discovery by Geller and Huchra[4] that galaxies are grouped in huge wall-like structures and voids, some of them close to half-a-billion light years across (see *Figure* 3.3). The astronomer J. Einasto, discussing more recent research results, comments:

> Here, using a new compilation of available data on galaxy clusters, we present evidence for a quasiregular three-dimensional network of rich

[1] M. S. Turner and A. Tyson, 'Cosmology at the Millennium', *Reviews of Modern Physics,* 1999, 71, pp. S145–64

[2] T. R. Lauer and M. Postman, 'The Motion of the Local Group', *Astrophysical Journal,* 1994, 425, pp. 418–38.

[3] M. Strauss *et al.,* 'Can Standard Cosmological Models Explain the Observed Abell Cluster Bulk Flow?', *Astrophysical Journal,* 1995, 444, pp. 507–19.

[4] M. J. Geller and J. P. Huchra, 'Cosmic Cartographers Find "Great Wall" ', *Science News,* 1989, 136, p. 340.

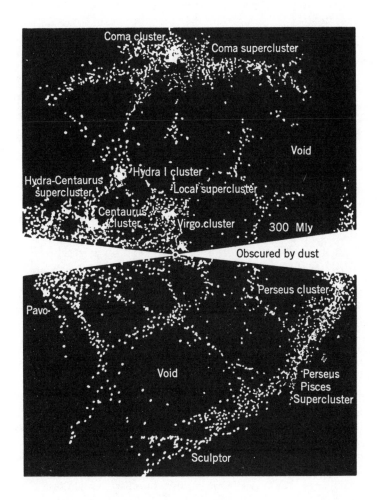

Figure 3.3: Distribution of Nearby Galaxies
Our galaxy lies in the centre of this schematic representation, which spans 600 million light-years in space. Each dot represents a galaxy. Note the immense voids.
(From Michael Zeilik, *Conceptual Astronomy,* New York: John Wiley & Sons Inc., 1992.)

superclusters and voids, with the regions of high density separated by about 120 Megaparsecs [about 400 million light-years]. If this reflects the distribution of all matter (luminous and dark), then there must exist some hitherto unknown process that produces regular structure on large scales.[1]

It should be noted that background radiation had been predicted also by other theories. From estimates of the radiation emitted by stars, the British astronomer A. S. Eddington[2] calculated the temperature of interstellar space to be 2 – 3 degrees Kelvin, due to heating caused by starlight. Finlay-Freundlich, on the basis of his tired-light explanation of the cosmic redshift, had predicted the temperature of inter-galactic space to be between 1.9 and 6 degrees Kelvin.[3]

Narlikar notes that several astrophysical processes could produce energy densities of the right size: the galactic magnetic field, cosmic rays, and starlight.[4] As noted above, it was pointed out by Burbidge and Hoyle that if all the helium observed in the universe were made in stars, the starlight so generated would have the same energy density as the microwave background. It has been suggested by Narlikar and others that long slender grains of graphite, or microscopic bacteria, in interstellar space would alter this light so that its spectrum would be similar to that of the observed background radiation. Such mechanisms were used in various updated versions of steady-state cosmology and in Hoyle's eternal 'little-big-bang universe', where an infinite succession of 'little big bangs' interact with already existent matter to form clumps from which stars and galaxies coalesce.[5]

A cosmological model of S. V. M. Clube,[6] involving hyper-massive nuclei in galaxies and a cold 'material vacuum', supposedly provides a natural explanation of the microwave background. As already

[1] J. Einasto *et al.*, 'A 120-Mpc Periodicity in the Three-dimensional Distribution of Galaxy Superclusters', *Nature*, 1997, *385*, 139.

[2] A. S. Eddington, *The Internal Constitution of the Stars,* Cambridge: The University Press, 1926, pp. 371, 377.

[3] E. Finlay-Freundlich, 'Red Shifts in the Spectrum of Celestial Bodies', *Philosophical Magazine,* 1954, *45*, pp. 303–19.

[4] J. V. Narlikar, 'Did the Universe Originate in a Big Bang?' *in* S. K. Biswas (ed.), *Cosmic Perspectives,* Cambridge: The University Press, 1989.

[5] F. Hoyle, *The Intelligent Universe.* New York: Holt, Rinehart & Winston, 1983.

[6] S. V. M. Clube, 'The Material Vacuum', *Monthly Notices of the Royal Astronomical Society,* 1980, *193*, p. 385.

noted, the tired-light theories account for the radiation in terms of re-radiation of the energy lost by light. On the other hand, Ellis accounts for the background radiation in terms of a hot gas at a second centre of the universe. Gentry appeals to a shell of hot hydrogen gas enclosing the galaxies of the visible universe.[1]

One advantage of the big-bang explanation is that it gives a simple explanation for the way that the background radiation is observed to vary with wavelength (it behaves like a perfectly efficient heat source, called a 'black body'). Other explanations usually have more difficulty accounting for this feature, though in Segal's static cosmology (see p. 50) the black-body form of the background radiation arises naturally as the equilibrium state of scattered photons .

Further Big-Bang Problems

By 1980, in spite of its initial successes, big-bang cosmology had encountered a number of perplexing theoretical problems. First there was the problem of galaxy formation. The uniformity of the background radiation implied that, shortly after the big bang, the energy was very smoothly distributed. How could this result in the galaxies, and even larger structures, that we see today?

Next there was the 'horizon' problem. The background radiation is uniform in all directions, implying that regions of space now apparently separated by billions of light years have the same physical conditions. Yet these regions are so far apart that light, or any other information, has not had enough time to travel between them. How, then, can they share the same properties, such as temperature and energy density?

Another puzzle was the 'flatness' problem. At present the universe seems to be nearly 'flat', its density being near the boundary between a closed universe and an open one (see *Figure* 3.4). If the density were just a little more than the critical amount, then the universe would have collapsed again long ago; if it were just a bit less then it would have dispersed too quickly for stars to form. According to Narlikar[2], the density just after the big bang could not have differed from the critical amount by more than 1 part in 10^{55} (1 followed by 55 zeros). How does one explain this extraordinary coincidence?

[1] Ellis, 'Is the Universe Expanding?'; Gentry, 'A New Redshift Interpretation'.
[2] Narlikar, 'Did the Universe Originate in a Big Bang?'

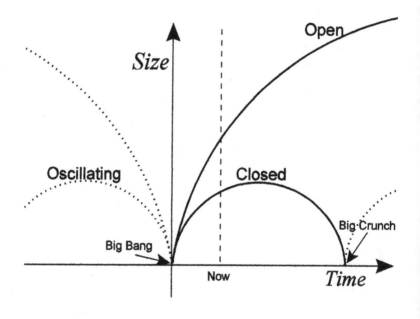

Figure 3.4: Size of the Universe versus Time.

After the Big Bang, an open universe will expand for ever; a closed universe will eventually contract into a Big Crunch, from which it may rebound as an oscillating universe. In either case, the Big Bang may have been preceded by a previous contraction.

1. Inflation

To solve these, and other, problems the concept of 'inflation' was introduced by Alan Guth. This concept arose from considerations of certain 'grand unified theories' which posit that, at extremely high temperatures, the nuclear and electromagnetic forces merge into a single force. Such high temperatures would prevail for the first 10^{-35} seconds (scientific shorthand for 1 shifted 35 places to the right of the decimal point, or 0.00000000000000000000000000000000001 of a second!) after the big bang. At that point certain regions of the universe entered a peculiar 'false vacuum' state, in which gravity became repulsive rather than attractive. As a result, these regions underwent a brief but huge expansion, or 'inflation', with expansion speeds much greater than the speed of light. One such region, which started off as a tiny region much smaller than an atom and ended up the size of a grapefruit an instant later, supposedly became our universe. According to this view, our observable universe is just a tiny bubble in a vastly greater cosmos.

Inflation explained the formation of galaxies. According to quantum physics, any energy field constantly fluctuates in intensity at the subatomic level, like waves on the surface of a lake. Inflation would make these fluctuations large enough to serve as seeds for stars and galaxies.

The very rapid expansion due to inflation also seemed to solve the 'horizon' problem. According to inflation, the region from which the observable universe emerged was so small that energy exchanges would have already made it homogeneous.

Further, inflation also solved the 'flatness' problem. Just as blowing up a beach ball to a thousand times its size would make its surface appear flatter to a nearby observer, so inflation would flatten out our region of the universe, yielding a density very close to the critical value.

Although inflation soon became an integral part of big bang cosmology, there are growing doubts about its viability.[1] A prime

---

[1] *See* Roger Penrose, 'Difficulties With Inflationary Cosmology', *Annals of the New York Academy of Sciences,* 1989, 571, pp. 249–64, *and* J. Earman and J. Mosterin, 'A Critical Look at Inflationary Cosmology', *Philosophy of Science,* 1999, 66.

difficulty is that inflation predicts the matter-energy density of the universe to be precisely at the critical level, whereas observations indicate a much smaller value. Another shortcoming is that there is no unique inflationary mechanism; many different inflationary scenarios have been devised, contrived to fit changing observational data. In fact, there seem to be so many open parameters that inflation can explain almost any given set of observations. Further, inflation depends on a variety of hypothetical entities in particle physics, such as the hypothetical Higgs field, that have not yet been observed.

2. Galaxy Formation

The early density fluctuations arising through inflation, and from which future galaxies were to form, should have left an imprint on the CMBR. Much excitement was generated on 23 April 1992 when, after a lengthy search, American astronomers announced that they had detected small variations in the CMBR. These were immediately interpreted as relics of lumpy structures that existed shortly after the birth of the universe. This discovery was hailed as a decisive confirmation of the big-bang theory of the origin of the universe. As reported the next day in the *International Herald Tribune*, the famous Cambridge cosmologist Stephen Hawking exclaimed, 'It is the discovery of the century, if not of all time', and George Smoot, leader of the research team that made the discovery, commented, 'It's like looking at God.'

Yet, in spite of such euphoria, difficulties remained. For one, the observed ripples were much smaller than originally predicted.[1] For such tiny seeds to grow into galaxies and the huge structures of galaxies that have recently been discovered would require much more time than big-bang cosmology allowed.

To solve the problem of galaxy formation, the existence of huge amounts of invisible matter, which had left no CMBR imprint, was postulated. If, in the early universe, such invisible matter were highly clumped, it could provide centres of strong gravitational attraction without disturbing the uniformity of the CMBR.

---

[1] Martin Rees, 'Ripples from the Edge of Time', *Guardian Weekly*, 3 May 1992, p. 11.

3. Missing Mass

There was further evidence for missing mass. The actual density of the universe, divided by the critical density needed to close the universe, is called 'Omega'. The observable mass in the universe yields an Omega of about 0.01, that is, one percent of the mass needed to close the universe. On the other hand, high orbital motion around galaxies and within galaxy clusters imply the existence of unseen, or 'dark', matter corresponding to an Omega of about 0.3.[1]

It was initially thought that the missing dark matter consisted of ordinary matter in the form of dust, black holes, and dim comets, planets, stars and galaxies. However, big-bang element-formation calculations indicated that ordinary matter, consisting of baryons (mainly neutrons and protons) cannot exceed 10% of the critical density. More baryons would have resulted in the formation of more helium than is observed. Hence ordinary matter yields an Omega of less than 0.1. It follows either that the big-bang model cannot account for the observed abundances of the light elements or that most of the matter in the universe consists of esoteric, non-baryonic matter. Most cosmologists have opted for the latter.

But what form could the missing matter take? A leading non-baryonic contender was the fast-moving ('hot') neutrino. Although such particles are known to exist, they interact very weakly with normal matter, making them very difficult to detect. However, neutrino-dominated models have their own problems. The main one is that the fast-moving neutrinos would have taken too long to settle down into galaxies.[2]

Thus theorists have concentrated on slowly moving ('cold'), dark ('hard to observe'), types of strange, non-baryonic matter. Since no stable cold-dark-matter particles have ever been detected, a host of esoteric hypothetical particles have been invented. These include such exotic concoctions as gravitons, photinos, axions, and WIMPS (for Weakly Interacting Massive Particles). Whether any of these actually exist, and in the needed proportions, remains to be seen.

[1] Peter Coles, 'The End of the Old Model Universe', *Nature*, 1998, *393* (25 June 1998), p. 741.
[2] John Horgan, 'Universal Truths', *Scientific American*, Oct.1990, pp. 109–17.

A study of galaxy clusters has found that baryonic matter forms a larger fraction of the total mass than predicted by inflationary cosmology.[1] This is bad news for big-bang cosmology. More bad news has come from the research of Ben Moore who has found cold-dark-matter models of galaxies to be fundamentally incompatible with recent observations of dwarf galaxies.[2]

These difficulties are further increased by the prediction of inflation theory that Omega should be exactly 1; there should be just enough matter to eventually stop the current expansion. This requires even larger amounts of 'missing' mass.

4. Acceleration

As the universe expands, the pull of gravity should act as a brake, slowing down the expansion rate. Since the light we now receive from distant galaxies corresponds to an earlier epoch, it should show a higher rate of expansion. Recent surveys, however, indicate that the deceleration of the universe is much smaller than that expected for Omega close to 1, and that expansion may even be accelerating.[3] This has led to the re-introduction of a 'cosmological constant', also called 'Lambda', which corresponds to a repulsive force that counter-acts gravity, as mentioned earlier.

In the newer models, Lambda acts like a kind of matter with very strange properties. It corresponds to a uniform energy density that bends space in the same way matter does. Yet it also has a negative pressure which, unlike gravity, tends to expand the universe and causes the cosmic acceleration. This energy density is caused not by matter or radiation but by a mysterious hypothetical property of 'empty' space. Since Lambda acts like matter, it causes an increase in Omega. Many cosmologists prefer a model where the total Omega is 1, precisely the critical value, with 0.3 contributed by matter and radiation, and a further 0.7 due to Lambda. This makes space flat and satisfies the prediction of inflation. Unfortunately, the existence of a Lambda of the required size is not explicable in terms of current

---

[1] S. D. M. White et al., 'The Baryon Content of Galaxy Clusters: A Challenge to Orthodox Cosmology', Nature, 1993, 366, p. 429.

[2] B. Moore, 'Evidence Against Dissipationless Dark Matter from Observations of Galaxy Haloes', Nature, 1994, 370, pp. 629–31.

[3] Coles, 'The End of the Old Model Universe.'

particle physics. Calculations in particle physics of the vacuum energy produced as the universe cools predict a Lambda about 10^{120} times greater than the observed density of matter.[1] According to Nobel laureate Steven Weinberg:

> This must be the worst failure of an order-of-magnitude estimate in the history of science.[2]

Many cosmologists worry about this huge discrepancy. John Earman, noting that some physicists consider the cosmological constant to be the biggest problem in all physics, writes:

> Some authors propose to resolve the problem by appealing to wormholes in spacetime; others postulate a mechanism involving a phase transition in $N = 8$ supergravity; others resort to the anthropic principle. To our mind, these moves are symptoms of desperation.[3]

Recently, in an effort to solve the Lambda problem and to avoid the problems created by inflation, John Barrow[4] and Albrecht and Magueijo[5] have postulated that the speed of light was much greater in the distant past. Barrow shows that this can also solve the horizon and flatness problems. One advantage this has over inflation is that it does not require huge amounts of hypothetical strange gravitationally-repulsive forms of matter.

5. More Puzzles

Recently astronomers have observed a second type of background radiation. This is in the infra-red region of the spectrum and, according to big-bang cosmology, is thought to date from a previously unseen period of the universe – between the release of the microwave background and the formation of the earliest known galaxies, about a billion years later. George Musser reports that this radiation is 2.3 times as bright as the visible light in the universe.[6] It implies that the universe is filled with enormous amounts of dust. The source of the

---

[1] Coles, 'The End of the Old Model Universe.'
[2] S. Weinberg, *Dreams of a Final Theory*, New York: Pantheon, 1992.
[3] Earman and Mosterin, 'A Critical Look at Inflationary Cosmology'.
[4] J. D. Barrow, 'Cosmologies with Varying Light-Speed', *Physical Review D,* 1999, 59, 043515.
[5] A. Albrecht and J. Magueijo, 'A Time Varying Speed of Light as a Solution to Cosmological Problems', *Physical Review D,* 1999, 59, 043516.
[6] G. Musser, 'Glow in the Dark', *Scientific American,* March 1998, 278, p. 18.

radiation is as yet unidentified, but it is presumed to come from distant galaxies. According to Musser, the unexpectedly bright background suggests star formation got going faster and generated more energy than current models predict.

Finally, there are difficulties concerning observed objects with high red shifts. In big-bang cosmology, high red shifts are presumed to indicate large distances and early formation times. The cold-dark-matter model predicts that most galaxies take at least several billion years to form. This corresponds to a red shift of 4 or 5. Yet recent observations of a very small patch of sky with the Hubble Space Telescope found fourteen galaxies with red shifts between 5 and 10, and another 5 candidates with red shifts larger than 10.[1] At a red shift of 10, the galaxies are seen when the universe presumably was only 9% of its current size and probably just a few hundred million years old. Such rapid formation of galaxies and stars is hard to account for in big-bang models.

A related problem concerns the appearance of these supposedly young objects. They often show surprisingly little evidence of 'evolution'. For example, NASA reports that the Hubble Space Telescope found distant elliptical galaxies that looked remarkably similar to today's galaxies.[2] It considered this to be a paradox: grown-up galaxies in an infant universe. The same source also found a cluster of galaxies at a high red shift and quotes astronomer Duccio Maccheto of the European Space Agency:

> The very presence of the cluster shows that these large structures already existed two billion years after the Big Bang. This is unexpected and counter to many theories of cluster and galaxy formation.

For further difficulties with big bang cosmology, I refer the interested reader to the papers by Arp, Berlinski, La Violette, Lerner and Mitchel in the bibliography, and further references found therein.

Basic Cosmological Assumptions

The existence of a wide variety of cosmological models indicates that it is not a simple matter to construct a cosmological model from our

---

[1] G. Schilling, 'Galaxies Seen at the Universe's Dawn', *Science*, 1999, *283*, p. 21.
[2] NASA, 'Hubble Uncovers New Clues to Galaxy Formation', http://opposite.stsci.edu/pubinfo/background-text/galxpdx.txt, 1994

observations of the universe. Not only are the observations explicable in many different ways, but also the actual observations themselves are of an incomplete, limited nature. The creation of a model of the physical universe as a whole requires us to make a number of basic assumptions that are often difficult to verify.

What kind of assumptions are generally made in cosmology? They may include such broad ones as the assumption of the universal validity of local physics (including, particularly, general relativity), the assumption that we occupy a typical position in the universe, and the assumption that the universe can be represented by a four-dimensional space-time continuum.[1] Also more detailed assumptions may be added, such as the motion interpretation of the galactic red shifts or the existence of a past big-bang singularity.

Two assumptions are so fundamental to most cosmological models that they warrant a more detailed discussion at this point.

1. Induction

Consider first the various assumptions concerning uniformity. It is generally assumed that the *principle of induction* is valid, that the laws of physics observed here and now are universally applicable. Moreover, it is commonly taken for granted that explanations of structure must be given in terms of these laws.

While such uniformity principles may seem reasonable enough, they are not unproblematic. The justification of induction is one of the outstanding problems in the philosophy of science. As the British philosopher David Hume pointed out in 1739, there is no compelling reason for believing it. Induction cannot be justified by observation, since the unobserved universe is, by definition, unobserved. Nor can it be justified by logic, since there is no logical reason why the universe must behave uniformly. Hence the universe beyond our experience may be quite different from what we might expect.

Induction may be the simplest, most convenient extrapolation. But that in itself does not guarantee its truthfulness. After all, how can we be sure that simple (or beautiful, useful, etc.) theories are more

---

[1] These are discussed, for example, by William Stoeger, 'Contemporary Cosmology and Implications for the Science-Religion Dialogue' *in* J. R. Russell, (ed.), *Physics, Philosophy and Theology: A Common Quest for Understanding*, Vatican City: Vatican Observatory Press, 1988.

likely to be true? One is still faced with the difficult matter of identifying and justifying valid criteria for theory selection.

While induction is a problem also for other sciences, the situation is worse for cosmology, which strives to depict and explain the entire history of the physical universe. Most other sciences are much more closely tied to observation and experimentation. Furthermore, in cosmology one must assume, not merely that locally observed physical laws apply everywhere and always, but also that these laws remain valid under rather extreme circumstances, such as the tremendous temperatures and pressures near the big-bang singularity.

As we have seen, some cosmologies relax the induction assumption to some degree by postulating changing physical constants, such as the gravitational constant or the speed of light. Yet even here it is generally assumed that the time-dependence of the constant is governed by some higher law, taken to be universally applicable.

As a more radical alternative to induction, several astronomers have noted the possibility that the universe might have been created instantaneously in the recent past. This notion will be discussed in more detail in a later chapter.

2. The Cosmological Principle

A second assumption commonly made concerns an observational feature. The universe about us appears to be remarkably 'isotropic', that is, it looks roughly the same in all directions. One obvious explanation is that we are near the centre of a spherically-symmetric universe. But such a solution is distasteful to modern cosmologists. As Ellis remarks:

> In ages by, the assumption that the Earth was at the centre of the universe was taken for granted. As we know, the pendulum has now swung to the opposite extreme; this is a concept that is anathema to almost all thinking men . . . It is due to the Copernican-Darwinian revolution in our understanding of the nature of man and his position in the universe. He has been dethroned from the exalted position he was once considered to hold.[1]

[1] G. F. R. Ellis, 'Cosmology and verifiability', *Quarterly Journal of the Royal Astronomical Society,* 1975, 16, pp. 250.

It would certainly be consistent with the present observations that we were at the centre of the universe, and that, for example, galaxies were distributed spherically symmetrically about us in shells of increasing density as their distance from us increased. Although mathematical models for such earth-centred cosmologies have occasionally been investigated, they have not been taken seriously; in fact, the most striking feature of mainstream cosmology is how this obvious possibility has been completely discounted.

Instead, to explain the observed isotropy, the *Cosmological Principle* is adopted. This postulates that we occupy a typical, rather than a special, position in the universe. It assumes that all hypothetical observers throughout the universe would, at the same cosmic time, observe roughly the same features of the universe. This implies that the universe can have no edges, since an observer near the edge would not see an isotropic distribution of galaxies. It follows that the universe is either a finite, spherically-curved space or infinite.

Since we can observe the universe from only one position – ours – there can be no direct evidence for the cosmological principle. There is, however, an indirect test. If the cosmological principle holds, then the universe should be spatially homogeneous; the distribution of matter should then be roughly the same throughout the universe.

Observations, however, indicate that the distant galaxies are not distributed uniformly in space. Now, to some degree this may be expected, since the more distant galaxies presumably represent an earlier epoch when the universe was denser and the galaxies were closer together. However, even after correcting for this effect, the density of galaxies appears to be a function of their distance from us. At first sight this would seem to refute the cosmological principle. Nonetheless, it has been saved from falsification by postulating that galaxies evolve in time. It is conjectured that, in the past, the galaxies were not merely closer together but were also more numerous than now. The presumed evolution rate is adjusted so as to make the universe homogeneous. Again quoting Ellis:

> The assumption of spatial homogeneity has inevitably been made, and has led to the conclusion that the population of radio sources [galaxies observed via radio-telescopes] evolves extremely rapidly. What has

therefore happened is that an unproven cosmological assumption has been completely accepted and has been used to obtain rather unexpected information about astrophysical processes.[1]

In short, the cosmological principle is a metaphysical belief that is saved from falsification by the introduction of *ad hoc* auxiliary theories, such as the alleged rapid evolution of galaxies.

The cosmological principle does have the advantage of yielding a model which is relatively simple from a mathematical point of view. But simple theories are not necessarily more accurate than more complex ones. It is possible to construct other models based upon different assumptions. For example, as we have already noted, steady-state cosmology is based on the Perfect Cosmological Principle: the assumption that the universe is roughly the same not only in space *but also in time*. Or one could drop the cosmological principle altogether and build models that place us near the centre of a spherically-symmetric universe. Several such cosmologies have been constructed. Indeed, recent observations indicate that the universe is open, ruling out the closed, finite universe with no edges. The cosmological principle implies that an open universe is infinite. Since inflationary cosmology, on the other hand, posits a finite universe, a number of inflationary big-bang models have recently dropped the cosmological principle. Cosmologist Andrei Linde, for example, in his eternal, self-reproducing universe, calculates that the universe will be non-homogeneous, with each observer being near the centre of a spherical hole in the density distribution. The observers are so far separated that each will consider himself to be at the centre of the world.[2]

Finally, it should be kept in mind that the cosmological principle is based on the assumed homogeneity of the universe. Recent observations of huge collections of galaxies and of large-scale motions of galaxies (discussed earlier in this chapter) suggest that the universe may not be as homogenous as is generally assumed.

---

[1] *Ibid.*, p. 250.
[2] A. Linde *et al.*, 'Do We Live in the Center of the World?', *Physics Letters B*, 1995, 345, pp. 203–10.

The Problem of Verification

As we have noted, some of the most basic assumptions in cosmology are of an essentially unverifiable nature. Verification can be a problem also for more specific aspects of cosmological models.

Oldershaw distinguishes between two types of untestability:

1. *Untestability of the First Kind*: A theory that is untestable because it cannot generate definitive testable predictions or whose predictions are impossible to test is *inherently* untestable.

2. *Untestability of the Second Kind*: A theory that has many adjustable parameters or is in general modifiable in an *ad hoc* manner is *effectively* untestable.

Many of the basic features of big-bang cosmology, the currently favoured model, are inherently untestable. The most critical events supposedly occurred within 10^{-25} seconds after the big bang. Yet, as Oldershaw notes,[1] in principle we cannot obtain direct information on the state of the universe prior to the decoupling of radiation and matter at 10^{13} seconds after the big bang. The latest inflationary big-bang models are heavily dependent upon particle physics, which in turn involves more unverifiable theoretical entities. Many theories of the new physics require extra dimensions: 5 to 26 dimensions is typical and about 950 dimensions is the latest record. Yet there is no known way to test empirically for the existence of these extra dimensions. A further difficulty is that conditions in the early universe (tremendously high temperatures and pressures) are such that they cannot be reproduced elsewhere. Hence the particle physics being used cannot be tested independently.

Burbidge comments, 'But since there is no way of testing the inflation hypothesis by direct observation, it has always seemed to me that it also is an idea with only a metaphysical basis.'[2]

There are also numerous cases involving untestability of the second kind. Particle physics has been applied to overcome various observational shortcomings of big-bang cosmology. However, most

---

[1] R. L. Oldershaw, 'The New Physics – Physical or Mathematical Science?', *American Journal of Physics*, 1988, 56, pp. 1075–81.
[2] G. Burbidge, 'Modern Cosmology: the Harmonious and the Discordant Facts', *in* B. R. Iyer (ed.), *Highlights in Gravitation and Cosmology*, Cambridge: The University Press, 1988.

of the proposed scenarios are decidedly *ad hoc*. The standard model of particle physics has more than twenty parameters (such as particle masses and coupling strengths of the forces) that cannot be uniquely derived and are thus freely adjustable. There are currently at least half a dozen superstring theories. Many of the problems in particle physics are 'solved' *ad hoc* by inventing new concepts, such as the 'Higgs mechanism', renormalization, and 'colour'.[1]

The cosmologist P. J. E. Peebles has wryly remarked:

> The big news so far is that particle physicists seem to be able to provide initial conditions for cosmology that meet what astronomers generally think they want without undue forcing of the particle physicist's theory. Indeed I sometimes have the feeling of taking part in a vaudeville skit: 'You want a tuck in the waist? We'll take a tuck. You want a massive weakly interacting particle? We have a full rack . . . ' This is a lot of activity to be fed by the thin gruel of theory and negative observational results, with no prediction and experimental verification of the sort that, according to the usual rules of physics, would lead us to think that we are on the right track.[2]

Also, in cosmology proper, *ad hoc* proposals abound. For example, at least three elaborate theories have been constructed to explain the recently discovered large-scale structure in the universe: superconducting cosmic strings, biased galaxy formation in a WIMP-dominated universe, and 'double' inflation. Similarly, numerous ingenious proposals purport to account for the vast amounts of alleged 'missing mass' in the universe.

Summary

A number of important conclusions can be drawn from our survey of modern cosmology.

1. Deficiencies in Big-Bang Cosmology

First, big-bang cosmology, even though it is currently by far the most popular cosmology and even though it is often presented as undoubtedly true, is beset with a number of serious observational and theoretical difficulties.

---

[1] See Oldershaw, 'The New Physics'.
[2] P. J. E. Peebles, Book Review: *Inner Space/Outer Space – The Interface between Cosmology and Particle Physics,* by E.W. Kolb, *Science,* 1987, 235, p. 372.

On the observational side, we recall such observational puzzles as anomalous red shifts, the departure from the linear Hubble law, difficulties in accounting for the observed elemental abundances, huge structures of galaxies and other major inhomogeneities, the large drift of galaxies with respect to the background radiation, the apparent acceleration of galaxies, and mature galaxies with high red shifts.

On the theoretical side, we recall the lack of energy conservation, the problem of the hypothetical inflation mechanism, the alleged existence of huge amounts of strange, invisible matter, the problem of the cosmological constant, Lambda, the problem of the formation of galaxies and huge structures of galaxies, and so on. Many proposed theoretical explanations are inherently unverifiable.

At the moment it is not clear how these can all be satisfactorily resolved. Moreover, we have not yet addressed further fundamental problems associated with the alleged big-bang singularity, a subject to be discussed in the next chapter. In short, both empirically and theoretically, big-bang cosmology lacks cohesion and plausibility.

This does not mean that big-bang cosmology cannot be saved. In principle, it is always possible to salvage a favoured cosmological model. One can always devise suitable *ad hoc* modifications to the theoretical model to make it conform to the observational data. Thus, for example, big-bang cosmology was saved from falsification by inventing inflation, which involved very contrived scenarios based on a very hypothetical Higgs field. Predictions of inflation for an Omega of 1 were saved by inventing huge amounts of missing mass. When it was shown that this missing mass cannot be ordinary matter, a whole host of esoteric particles were invented, none of which have been actually observed, and so on.

One is reminded of Ptolemy's epicycles, and subsequent attempts in medieval cosmology to better explain the observations by postulating epicycles upon epicycles. Given the number of free parameters in particle physics and the fertile imagination of cosmologists, it may well be that the future will yield a big-bang cosmological model that will surmount all of the current difficulties. In practice, moreover, a favoured cosmological model is not discarded, even if currently falsified by data, until a more acceptable alternative is found.

2. The Possibility of Alternative Cosmologies

This brings us to our second conclusion, the possibility of alternative cosmologies. As we saw, all the observational features have multiple theoretical interpretations. This has led to a host of alternative cosmologies. Many of these have been mentioned in our discussion of the red shift and background radiation, many more can be found in the volume *Progress in New Cosmologies* by Arp, Keys and Rudnicki, listed in the bibliography, and references cited there.

Our discussion has highlighted the shortcomings of big-bang cosmology only because it is currently the majority choice. It should be stressed that all the alternative cosmologies have serious problems of their own to overcome. For example, most of the alternative interpretations of the red shifts are highly speculative. And most alternative explanations for the observed abundances and background radiation seem to involve at least as much fudging and special pleading as does big-bang cosmology.

Yet these cosmologies cannot simply be rejected as false. Here, too, one cannot rule out future improvements. Indeed, one suspects that, were alternative cosmologies to be the recipients of as much ingenuity and research funding as has gone into big-bang cosmology, they could likewise be suitably modified to 'save the phenomena'.

Currently there is no cosmological model that offers a simple explanation, in terms of well-established physical laws, of all the observational data. With the recent advent of the Hubble Space Telescope, and other remarkable advances in electronic instrumentation and computing, we are on the verge of a new era in astronomy. A proliferation of new, more reliable data on distant parts of the universe can be expected in the next decade. No doubt future observations will resolve some current problems while at the same time raising new ones, leading to the development of new cosmological models that differ significantly from current big-bang cosmology. It is therefore prudent not to equate any current cosmology with the actual history of the cosmos.

Nevertheless, the intrinsic, unavoidable epistemic gap between actual observations and the hypothetical cosmological models trying to explain these will ensure that there will continue to be a variety of cosmological models.

3. The Necessity of Presuppositions

How are we to choose among competing cosmologies? Our third conclusion is that any cosmological model must necessarily rest on various assumptions that are essentially unverifiable. The justification of these basic presuppositions must thus come from subjective, extra-scientific considerations. As we noted in the first chapter, scientific theorizing is guided largely by our prior philosophical and religious beliefs. Particularly in cosmology, where we attempt to explain literally everything, we construct theoretical models that are consistent with our most basic convictions.

It is therefore crucial that we be aware of the underlying philosophical presuppositions involved in the construction, assessment and selection of cosmological models.

4

Cosmology and God's Existence

What does the existence of the cosmos imply about the existence of God? If big-bang cosmology were true, would it constitute a proof for the existence of God? Various theological implications have been drawn from modern cosmology. Foremost among these are a number of proofs for the existence of God.

Rational proofs for the existence of God date back to at least the time of Plato. These proofs can be grouped into four basic types. The *ontological argument* (from the Greek *ontos*, being) is based on the notion that the very concept of an absolutely perfect Being demands that such a Being exists. The *moral argument* asserts that the existence of a moral law implies the existence of a moral-law giver. The *cosmological argument* (from the Greek *cosmos*, world) postulates that there must be a prior Cause to explain the existence of the universe. The *teleological argument* (from the Greek *telos*, design or purpose) contends that the apparent design within the world points to an intelligent designer.

Virtually all of the major philosophers have discussed at least some of these proofs. My prime concern is not to examine in detail the philosophical subtleties involved, but to concentrate on the part played by cosmological factors. Thus I shall consider pertinent aspects of only the latter two proofs: the cosmological argument, based on evidence pointing towards a beginning of the universe, and the teleological argument, based on evidence for design within the universe.

My intention in what follows is not to undermine a rationally-grounded belief in God but to caution against excessive confidence, on the one hand in human reasoning on these matters, and, on the other, in big-bang cosmology, as a basis for Christian apologetics. As I hope to show, such confidence can leave us dangerously exposed to counter-arguments designed to refute Christian theism.

The Cosmological Argument

The cosmological argument is probably the most popular of the proofs. Over the years many different versions of it have been presented. Geisler and Corduan affirm that only the cosmological argument offers hope for a theistic proof; much of their philosophy of religion rests upon its presumed validity.[1]

Our focus will be on the *Kalam* Cosmological Argument, which aims to demonstrate that the universe was created a finite time ago by a personal Creator. The argument is grounded upon the supposed impossibility of an actual infinity of past events. Many of the arguments against an actual infinity can be traced back to Aristotle, although the Christian philosopher John Philoponus seems to have been the first to apply them, in 529 AD, to a demonstration of the finite age of the universe.[2] Philoponus' proofs for creation were taken up and further developed in the ninth and tenth centuries by a number of Islamic philosophers of the Kalam school, becoming thus known as the *Kalam* cosmological argument.[3]

In recent times it has been defended by several Christian apologists, including William Craig[4] and J. P. Moreland[5]. It boils down to the following reasoning:

(1) The universe had a beginning.

(2) The beginning of the universe was caused.

[1] Norman L. Geisler and Winfried Corduan, *Philosophy of Religion,* Grand Rapids: Baker, 2nd ed., 1988, p. 150.

[2] Richard Sorabji, *Time, Creation and the Continuum*, Ithaca: Cornell University Press, 1983, p. 198.

[3] See H. A. Davidson, *Proofs for Eternity, Creation and the Existence of God in Medieval Islamic and Jewish Philosophy*, Oxford: The University Press, 1987, pp. 117–53.

[4] *The Kalam Cosmological Argument*, London: Macmillan, 1979, and 'Philosophical and Scientific Pointers to Creation *ex Nihilo*', *Journal of the American Scientific Affiliation*, 1980, 32, pp. 5–13.

[5] *The Creation Hypothesis*, Downers Grove: InterVarsity, 1994, pp. 18–23.

(3) That cause was personal.

In short, the finite past of the universe implies its *ex nihilo* creation by a personal Creator.

Our prime concern here is with step (1). Can it be proven, without appealing to the Bible, that the universe had a beginning? A number of philosophical and scientific arguments for a beginning have been developed. We shall examine the strengths and implications of several arguments against an infinite past.

Philosophical Arguments

The supposed impossibility of the actual infinite is central not only to the Kalam cosmological argument, but also to the cosmological argument as defended by Geisler and Corduan in their book *Philosophy of Religion*, which takes on a somewhat different form. We shall first address the question as to whether arguments against the actual infinite are in fact valid. Then, supposing they are, we shall consider various theological implications.

1. Is an Actual Infinity Impossible?

The most common objection to a beginningless past is that, to arrive at the present time, an infinite number of years must be crossed. This is held to be impossible since, if we start counting: 1, 2, 3 . . ., we could never reach infinity. The series of numbers counted would increase forever, but it would always be finite. Hence today would never arrive.[1]

This argument assumes that there exists a past year that is separated from the present by an infinity of years. But this is not the case for a beginningless past. If we number the past years, counting back from the present, as 0, -1, -2, . . ., then the set of past years corresponds to the set of negative numbers. The set as a whole is certainly infinite, but no two specific negative numbers are ever infinitely far apart. Infinity is a property of the set as a whole, not of any particular members of the set.

Moreover, if it were true that the universe must have had a beginning a finite number of years ago, which year would it be? For any finite year one might care to name, one could always add one to it. As there is no bound to the negative numbers, so likewise there need be no bound to the number of past years.

[1] See, for example, Moreland, *The Creation Hypothesis,* p. 19.

Craig has constructed a variety of further arguments against an actual infinite.[1] These can be grouped into three categories:

(1) It is impossible to add to an actually infinite collection.

(2) The fact that infinite collections are all of equal size leads to contradictions.

(3) a collection formed by adding one member after another cannot be actually infinite.

These arguments have been examined in detail by Quentin Smith[2] who finds them to be fallacious and who concludes that there is no *philosophical* objection to an infinite past (although he does believe that there are valid *scientific* objections to it). I will not repeat Smith's analysis, which I believe to be correct, only note a few major concerns.

I believe that the prime confusion arises from the fact that Craig often assesses infinite sets by criteria that properly apply only to finite sets. Infinite sets certainly have strange properties. Such a set is still the same size after we add another member, double the set, or even square it. Since we are used to dealing only with finite sets, these properties do seem almost unbelievable. Nevertheless, as demonstrated by Georg Cantor (1845–1918) and confirmed by modern mathematicians, trans-finite mathematics *is* logically consistent. Although a number of paradoxes can arise in the usage of infinite sets, these are generally a result of self-referential problems.

Craig notes that he is arguing only against an actual infinity in the real world and in no way wishes to undermine the concept of infinity as found in Cantorian trans-finite mathematics. But there actual infinity is only an idea:

> What I shall argue is that while the actual infinite may be a fruitful and consistent concept in the mathematical realm, it cannot be translated from the mathematical world into the real world, for this would involve counter-intuitive absurdities.[3]

He gives a number of illustrations, one being a library consisting of an infinite number of books. Such a library has some strange properties. For example, if we eliminate half of the books, say the odd-numbered ones, then we still have as many books as we started

[1] 'Philosophical and Scientific Pointers'.

[2] 'Infinity and the Past', *Philosophy of Science*, 1987, 54, pp. 63–75.

[3] Craig, *The Kalam Cosmological Argument*, p. 69.

with. Yet if we now loan out the remaining, even-numbered, books then we have nothing left, even though we have removed exactly the same number as before. Furthermore, Craig argues, if we add a book to an infinite library then we can see that the collection is increased by one. We do not have the same number of books as before, as should be the case for an infinite set. He concludes that such examples serve to illustrate that an actual infinite cannot exist in the real world.

Does this argument really demonstrate the impossibility of an actual infinity in the real world? I think not. The above operations on books could also be done on, say, the positive numbers. Remove the odd ones and you still have an infinity left; remove now also the even ones and nothing remains. Or take the even numbers, which form an infinite set, and you can still add any odd number to it, leaving us still with an infinite set. If these operations are permissible for numbers, why not also for books? One might counter that one is an intellectual abstraction, whereas the other is a collection of concrete items. Yet, in essence, this should not affect the mathematical operations involved. Since one could set up a one-to-one correspondence between integers and books in a library (or events in time), it follows that likewise an actual infinity of books (or events) need not involve any *logical* difficulties, however counter-intuitive such an actual infinite library might be.

Is it meaningful for us even to contemplate the occurrence of an actual infinity in the real world of our experiences? After all, within the limitations of our finite experiences, memories, and thoughts, we can never distinguish between the infinite and merely the very large. Even if we could eliminate half of the books in an infinite library, the remainder will still be beyond our ability to count and thus, in any practical sense, will be the same as what we started with. Since all our human experiences are finite, the real actual infinite is necessarily counter-intuitive. But that by itself does not render it impossible.

Since Craig has not shown why the mathematics of sets of concrete objects differs from that of abstract sets, it is inconsistent for him to ban an actual infinite for one but not for the other.

2. God and the Future

Suppose, for the sake of the argument, that the proofs against the actual infinite were valid. Such a ban on the actual infinite would have some awkward theological consequences. Consider, first of all, the question of future events. The Bible, in its description of the life hereafter, pictures it as a temporal existence, with flowing water and ripening fruit, where the saints shall reign for ever and ever (*Rev.* 22:1–5): a seemingly endless future time. Is this view of the future not ruled out by the arguments against an actual infinity of past events, which imply that the future must likewise be finite?

Craig argues that this need not be the case. The future differs from the past in that it is not an actual completed infinity; it is only *potentially* infinite, in the sense of being inexhaustible. A potential infinity is, according to Craig, permissible:

> A potential infinite is a collection that is increasing without limit but is at all times finite . . . it is not truly infinite – it is simply indefinite.[1]

Past events are real since they have actually occurred; future events, asserts Craig, do not actually exist because they have not (yet) occurred. At first sight such a past/future distinction seems valid enough. However, when applied to the omniscient God of orthodox theology (and it must be kept in mind that this is just a step in an alleged proof for the existence of such a God) it becomes problematic. After all, such a God knows the future as definitely as he knows the past. If the future is indeed endless, then to an omniscient God it exists as a definite actual infinity, rather than merely as an indefinite potential infinity. It would seem that to God an endless future would have the same status as a beginningless past. Both entail the notion that God has knowledge of an infinite set of events.

Thus the considerations leading to a finite past must similarly apply to the future. If Craig's argument against an actual infinity is valid it implies that God's knowledge of the future encompasses only a finite number of events. Hence either the future is finite, and there is a last event, or God's knowledge of the future is incomplete.

3. God and the Past

There are further difficulties. Craig's arguments against the real existence of an actual infinity are sufficiently general that they seem to apply, not only to the physical universe, but also to God himself. This must have significant implications for our understanding of God, who is generally considered in orthodox theology to be infinite.

---

[1] 'Philosophical and Scientific Pointers', p. 6.

For example, Craig's ban on the actual infinite implies that God's past must also be finite. Indeed, he comes to this conclusion:

> Prior to creation God would have to be changeless. Otherwise you would get an infinite series of past events in God's life, and we have seen that such an infinite series is impossible. So God would be changeless and hence, timeless prior to creation.[1]

It seems that Craig views God as being essentially 'frozen' for an infinite time before the first event. This seems to place rather stringent conditions on the nature of God, ruling out any succession of divine acts or thoughts prior to the creation of the present universe.

It is interesting that Craig applies the prohibition of an actual infinity only to *events*, and not to the passage of time itself. He does allow for a past infinity of time before the creation of the physical world. Is this consistent? If an infinite duration of time is to be distinguished from a single unit of time then one must have the everlasting passage of time from one unit to the next, yielding an infinite number of units. Perhaps it is thought that, in the absence of physical events to measure time, we are not confronted with an actual infinity. But, surely, an omniscient God would know of any passage of time. To God, it would seem, even the passage of a unit of time is something which 'happens' and thus should count as an event. If God has existed through a past infinity of time then an actual infinity of units of time has elapsed. It follows that God's knowledge of a past that consists of finite events embedded within infinite time must include knowledge of an actual infinity of past units of time.

In short, a ban on the actual infinite seems to place undue restrictions not only on the past, but also on the future, on God, and on time itself. Although there may be aspects of infinity that appear incomprehensible to us, it seems to me that, in the absence of watertight logical disproofs of actual infinity, the better course is to attribute this perceived deficiency to human finiteness rather than to confer undue constraints upon God and his attributes.

The Big-Bang Singularity

For the cosmological argument to work without placing unwarranted limitations on God it is necessary to make a proper distinction between Creator and creation. The demonstration of the finite past

[1] *Ibid.*, p. 12.

of the physical universe is therefore perhaps better based on physical, rather than logical, grounds. Two main lines of scientific evidence are often cited as proof for the beginning of the universe: the big-bang singularity and the second law of thermodynamics.

In big-bang cosmology the time $t = 0$ corresponds to a state of infinite density. What happened before this? How did this state arise? It seems to represent a barrier beyond which the laws of physics cannot be applied. A common interpretation is that the big bang marks the beginning of time as well as the beginning of the universe.

In a famous statement in 1951, Pope Pius XII referred to the big-bang theory as testifying to a beginning of the cosmos, thus confirming the need for a Creator.[1] Nor was Pius XII alone here; many Christians concur in taking the big-bang singularity as a proof for the existence of a Creator. Most vocal among these are William Craig and Hugh Ross.[2]

The theistic implication of the big-bang singularity has been drawn also by scientists who are by no means sympathetic to theism. Thus, for example, Hannes Alfven, who won the Nobel prize in physics in 1970, writes that 'the state of the singular point necessarily presupposes a divine creation'.[3] This, apparently, is one of the reasons why Alfven rejects the big bang. Similarly, the prominent astronomer Fred Hoyle, who is rather hostile to Christianity,[4] rejects the big-bang theory, not just on scientific grounds, but because an eternal universe fits in better with his atheistic beliefs. McMullin[5] notes that strong opposition to the big-bang model came also from Soviet cosmologists, who asserted that the notion of an absolute beginning was fundamentally incompatible with the Marxist-Leninist principles of dialectical materialism.

On the other hand, many cosmologists and theologians deny any such close connection between big-bang cosmology and theism. This

---

[1] See Ernan McMullin, 'How Should Cosmology Relate to Theology?' *in* A. R. Peacocke, *The Sciences and Theology in the Twentieth Century*, Stocksfield: Oriel Press, 1981, p. 30.

[2] See Ross, *The Creator and the Cosmos*, Colorado Springs: Navpress, 1993.

[3] 'Cosmology: Myth or Science?' *in* W. Yourgrau and A. D. Breck (eds.), *Cosmology, History, and Theology*, New York: Plenum Press, 1974, pp. 7, 12.

[4] See, for example, his *Ten Faces of the Universe*, San Francisco: Freeman, 1977.

[5] 'How Should Cosmology Relate to Theology?', p. 36–7.

raises the question of how compelling the big-bang evidence is. Does it really prove that the physical universe began a finite time ago? And, if so, does this necessarily have theistic implications?

1. The Accuracy of the Big-Bang Model

In our earlier discussion of big-bang cosmology we found that, despite various observational advantages, it still suffered from a number of observational and theoretical deficiencies. Moreover, many of its theoretical assumptions were inherently unverifiable. Also, the observational evidence could be explained via other, non-singularity models. The argument for a singularity must, therefore, first demonstrate the superiority of the big-bang model over its challengers. This will involve the establishment and justification of specific criteria for theory selection, as well as proof that the big-bang cosmology best fulfils these standards.

But what are these criteria? Simplicity and beauty are two standards that are sometimes cited. Yet the further question as to why simple or beautiful theories are more likely to be true is rarely addressed. Even if these standards were acceptable, it is not easy to assess which cosmological model measures up best. Supporters of the big bang, such as Craig and Ross, tend to minimize the problems for the big bang and to give undue weight to those for rival theories. Indeed, they often affirm that the big bang has been proven and that all alternatives have definitely been ruled out. Detractors of the big bang, of course, tend to do the opposite. The assessment of cosmological models is clearly a very subjective exercise.

Nevertheless, there is little doubt that at the present time a large majority of cosmologists favour big-bang cosmology. While this in itself does not prove it to be true, it has swayed popular opinion to accept big-bang cosmology. This first step in the theistic proof may therefore be acceptable for most people.

2. Limits of the Big-Bang Model

Although big-bang cosmology may be the current favourite, its supporters are not agreed on what happened near the supposed singularity, before the first fraction of a second. At this point everything becomes extremely speculative. Here big-bang theory faces a number of limits that are difficult, if not impossible, to overcome.

a. Singularity Proofs

The British cosmologists Stephen Hawking, George Ellis, and Roger Penrose have constructed a number of singularity theorems that purport to prove, applying general relativity under fairly general conditions, that the present universe originated from a past singularity. Although these theorems are often cited as proof of a past singularity, they are based on a number of assumptions that restrict the power of the theorems. For example, it is commonly assumed that the universe is quite homogeneous, with matter smoothly distributed. Hawking and Ellis, in discussing their singularity theorem, note that, because of local irregularities, it is quite possible that not all the universe originated from a single singularity:

> One might suggest therefore that prior to the present expansion there was a collapsing phase. In this, local inhomogeneities grew large and isolated singularities occurred. Most of the matter avoided the singularities and re-expanded to give the presently observed Universe.[1]

A somewhat later singularity theorem by Hawking and Penrose assumes there is no positive cosmological constant, which would act as a repulsive force counteracting gravity.[2] This condition is contradicted by recent observations indicating the existence of a large positive cosmological constant. Senovilla, in his detailed examination of assumptions made in the singularity proofs, has found many possible general relativistic cosmologies in which the universe did not begin in a big-bang singularity.[3] Hence the singularity proofs, even within the confines of general relativity, fall short of proving the existence of a past big-bang singularity.

b. Unknown Physics

A further problem is that near the singularity the pressure and temperature would have been so great that conventional physics would no longer apply. Current theories of matter are no longer valid here. Various new theories of particle physics have been proposed, but these are all very conjectural and unverifiable.

[1] S. W. Hawking and G. F. R. Ellis, 'The Cosmic Black-Body Radiation and the Existence of Singularities in Our Universe', *Astrophysical Journal*, 1967, *152*, p. 32.
[2] S. W. Hawking and R. Penrose, 'The Singularities of Gravitational Collapse and Cosmology', *Proc. Royal Society London A*, 1970, *314*, pp. 529-548.
[3] J. M. M. Senovilla, 'Singularity Theorems and Their Consequences', *General Relativity & Gravitation*, 1998, *30*, pp. 701-848.

Even before that, within 10^{-43} seconds after the singularity, at the so-called Planck time, the density would have been so huge that quantum effects must be taken into account. General relativity must then be replaced by an appropriate theory of quantum gravity. Unfortunately, nobody has yet been able to develop a workable model for quantum gravity. Thus, what happens before the Planck time is anyone's guess. It is interesting that Einstein himself never accepted the existence of the alleged singularity. Shortly before his death Einstein commented:

> The present relativistic theory of gravitation is based on a separation of the concepts of 'gravitational field' and of 'matter'. It may be plausible that the theory is for this reason inadequate for a very high density of matter. It may well be the case that for a unified theory there would arise no singularity . . . For large densities of field and of matter, the field equations and even the field variables which enter into them will have no real significance. One may not therefore assume the validity of the equations for very high density of field and of matter, and one may not conclude that the 'beginning of the expansion' must mean a singularity in the mathematical sense. All we have to realize is that the equations may not be continued over such regions.[1]

The theologically significant questions arise just beyond the limits of the big-bang model. As we approach the alleged first event the theory becomes increasingly more speculative, with a corresponding rapid loss in scientific consensus. Certainly, there can be no rigorous proof that the singularity must necessarily be reached or that the present expansion was not preceded by a contraction.

c. The Scales of Time

The very definition of time and its measurement can also be problematic. John Barrow points out that the time interval to a past singularity may be finite if measured in *proper time*, defined as time measured by a clock in gravitational freefall, but could be infinite if measured in accordance with some other definition of time.[2] For example, we could conceive of a clock that measured the change in the curvature of the universe. According to Barrow, in the most

---

[1] Albert Einstein, *The Meaning of Relativity*, 5th Edition, Princeton: The University Press, 1956.

[2] J. D. Barrow, *The World within the World*, Oxford: Clarendon Press, 1988, p. 235.

general type of relativistic universe the past singularity is reached in a finite proper time but with an infinite number of oscillations of the curvature. Hence, as determined by the curvature clock, it takes an infinite past time to reach the initial singularity. Even if we stick to proper time, this still leaves us with an infinite number of physical past *events* – the successive changes in curvature – to record.

d. Definition of space and time

There is a further limitation. According to quantum mechanics it is impossible to construct clocks to measure time intervals shorter than the Planck time (10^{-43} second) or to construct rulers to measure lengths smaller than the Planck length (10^{-33} cm). Many cosmologists believe a quantity that cannot be measured in principle is physically meaningless. Hence the notions of time and space no longer apply beyond the Planck limit. Thus, for example, Zhi and Xian assert that before the Planck time we have a world without time and space, that time and space come into being only at the Planck time.[1]

If time is no longer concrete, how can we ask what came 'before' the Planck time? A theist might respond that measurement constraints applying to man do not necessarily apply to an omniscient God. Hence, it may well be meaningful to consider time and space to exist before the Planck limit.

Yet, even in the absence of quantum effects, the meaning of time and space at the singularity can become a problem. There can really be no more talk of three-dimensional space if everything has been condensed into a point. Moreover, time and space are generally thought of in connection with matter and energy. Some cosmologists have thus postulated that time and space originated in the same bigbang event that brought about matter and energy.

According to Grunbaum the whole question of creation is a pseudo-problem since, in big-bang cosmology, time came into existence at the singularity, along with the universe.[2] Thus it is meaningless to ask what happened before $t = 0$, since there was no time then. One may postulate the existence of time before the singularity,

---

[1] Zhi, Fang Li and Xian, Li Shu, *Creation of the Universe*, Singapore: World Scientific, 1989, p. 149.

[2] Adolph Grunbaum, 'The Pseudo-Problem of Creation in Physical Cosmology', *Philosophy of Science,* 1989, 56, pp. 373–94.

but one should not expect the big-bang model to supply answers to questions that deny its assumptions.

Grunbaum's comment is pertinent to Craig's theistic proof in several ways. First, in order to prove that the universe was caused, Craig argues that whatever began to exist must have a cause. This fits in with our experience that nothing jumps, uncaused, into being. God, who has always existed, needs no cause. However, Craig's argument does assume there was a time in which the universe did not exist. According to Grunbaum this is inadmissible, since there was never a time when the universe did not exist. Time and the universe came into being together, so that the universe has existed at all times. Hence the rule that whatever began to exist must have a cause does not apply to the universe.

A second difficulty concerns Craig's argument that the cause of the universe was *personal*. Craig posits the existence of an infinite, eventless time before creation. Since all moments in such an infinite time are alike, it requires, he argues, a *personal* being to freely choose to create at any specific time in the absence of any features distinguishing one moment from another. Again, according to Grunbaum, such an alleged infinity of time before creation is inconsistent with big-bang cosmology.

These remarks should caution proponents of the cosmological argument not to rely too heavily on big-bang cosmology, with all its accompanying metaphysical baggage. Yet, although within the big-bang model the question of what happened before the singularity may be meaningless, this would not rule out the need for a Creator. It might do away with the need for a deistic God, a Watchmaker who leaves the world running by itself after creation. However, we are still left with the question as to why the universe, including time, came into existence and continues to exist. A Creator is still needed to sustain the cosmos.

3. Beginningless Possibilities

Not all cosmologists agree with Grunbaum's assertion that time began with the big bang. Many have objected to the notion that the universe has existed for only a finite time. Recall, for example, the variety of static cosmological models discussed in the previous chapter. Even within big-bang cosmology it is not necessary that the universe began at a singularity. Various big-bang models have been constructed that avoid a beginning in time.

a. Oscillating Universes

The earliest eternal alternative was based on the notion that the big-bang expansion could have been preceded by a contraction, by a Big Crunch. The Big Crunch would have destroyed any evidence of previous cycles, except, possibly, for some very general parameters such as the energy and entropy.

Such an eternal, oscillating universe has been advocated by a number of modern cosmologists, starting with the Dutch astronomer Willem de Sitter in 1931. It soon became evident, however, that such models have serious shortcomings. It was calculated, for example, that each new cycle yields an increase in the maximum size of the universe, with an accompanying increase in the time needed to complete a cycle. Extrapolating back into the past, the cycles become infinitely short in a finite time. Also, each cycle produces more radiation. If radiation accumulates, then the radiation currently observed allows no more than about one hundred previous cycles.[1] A similar result is also obtained from thermodynamics: if an infinite number of previous cycles have elapsed, each with increasing entropy, then the present cycle would be in a state of maximum entropy – but in fact it is now in a state of relatively low entropy. Thus even an oscillating universe, while allowing an infinite future, seemed to point towards a beginning some finite time in the past.

To evade a finite past, physicist John Wheeler has suggested that, at the end of each contracting phase, all the constants and laws of that cycle disappear and the universe is reprocessed, acquiring new constants and laws for the next cycle. No information is passed on to the next cycle. Thus no inference to a finite past can be made on the basis of the observations, laws, and constants of the present cycle.

In response, Quentin Smith[2] has objected that, while this may be logically possible, yet, since the new laws and constants cannot be predicted, it is preferable to follow the principle that physical laws and constants established for one domain should, in the absence of

[1] Quentin Smith, 'The Uncaused Beginning of the Universe', *Philosophy of Science*, 1988, 55, pp. 39–57.
[2] *Ibid.*, p. 43.

evidence to the contrary, be applied to other domains. While there may be some merit in Smith's criterion, it is again one of philosophical expediency rather than rational proof.

The Russian cosmologist Markov contends that the universe would transform into a vacuum when it comes close to the singularity. There would then be no particles and entropy would not be definable. Thus the universe could oscillate forever, with each new cycle starting afresh.[1]

One further difficulty, however, with an oscillating universe is that it requires that the universe be closed. The universe must be sufficiently dense so that gravitational attraction will eventually halt each expansion phase and turn it into a contraction. As we have noted earlier, present observational evidence favours an open universe rather than a closed one. In an open universe matter will continue expanding forever.

An open universe does allow for another possibility for evading a beginning in time. George Gamow suggested that the big-bang singularity was preceded by a corresponding eternal contraction. In his view the universe has existed from eternity, collapsing from a state of infinite rarification until it arrived at the big bang singularity, when the density became immensely great. At that point it rebounded, the contraction turning into the present expansion. Gamow's proposal avoided the drawbacks of the oscillatory universe, since now there was no problem with accumulation of radiation or entropy.[2]

But one difficulty does remain. How does one account for the 'bounce' from contraction to expansion? It seems natural that a contracting universe would, once it reached the state of maximum compression, bounce back into an expanding phase rather than remaining at the singularity. Considerations based on such general principles as the conservation of energy appear to point in that direction. Although doubt has been expressed by Guth and Sher about whether the conditions near the singularity would allow for the possibility of a bounce,[3] these objections applied specifically to a closed universe. It is not clear whether they would apply to an open

[1] M. A. Markov, 'Asymptotic Freedom and Entropy in a Perpetually Oscillating Universe', *Physics Letters*, 1983, *94A*, pp. 427–9.

[2] G. Gamow, 'Modern Cosmology', *Scientific American*, 1954, *190*, pp. 55–63.

[3] A. H. Guth and M. Sher, 'The Impossibility of a Bouncing Universe', *Nature*, 1983, *302*, pp. 505–7.

universe. On the other hand, cosmologists Israelit and Rosen[1] have developed scenarios that do allow for a bounce. Here also, questions cannot be answered definitely until a valid theory of quantum gravity is found.

b. Vacuum Fluctuation Models

It has been proposed by a number of cosmologists that the present universe emerged spontaneously from a pre-existent vacuum. Such a model was first presented by Edward Tryon.[2]

This model is based on quantum mechanics, in particular on the *uncertainty principle,* which states that at any time we can accurately measure either the position or motion of a small particle, but not both at once. According to this principle, particles can be spontaneously generated in a vacuum by random fluctuations of energy. The smaller the energy of the particle, the longer the particle can exist before disappearing again into the void. Tryon asserted that, in the universe as a whole, the positive energy of matter is exactly cancelled by the negative energy of gravity, so that the total energy of the universe is zero. According to the uncertainty principle, a particle of zero energy can exist forever. Hence, according to Tryon, the universe, being of zero energy, can last indefinitely long, a colossal 'free lunch'.

The Russian cosmologist Rozental has developed this into an eternal, infinite cosmology. The universe is seen as an infinite vacuum, boiling with energy fluctuations. Our present universe is just one of the larger fluctuations to emerge from the vacuum; in time it will again dissolve back into the vacuum.[3]

According to Linde, the only verifiable prediction, in principle, of the vacuum fluctuation models is that the universe must be closed.[4] If the universe were created by a vacuum fluctuation, then it cannot be infinitely large, as would be the case for an open universe, at least as predicted by the usual big-bang models. This is consistent with the inflationary big-bang model, but in conflict with the present observational evidence, which indicates that the density of matter in the

---

[1] M. Israelit and N. Rosen, 'A Singularity-free Cosmological Model in General Relativity', *Astrophysical Journal,* 1989, 342, p. 627.

[2] 'Is the Universe a Vacuum Fluctuation?', *Nature,* 1973, 246, pp. 396–7.

[3] I. L. Rozental, *Big Bang, Big Bounce,* Berlin: Springer Verlag, 1988.

[4] A. Linde, 'The Universe: Inflation out of Chaos', *New Scientist,* 7 March 1985, pp. 14–18.

universe is too small to close it. Thus unobservable missing matter, or energy, must be postulated to make up the difference.

c. Eternal Chaotic Cosmology

Markov and Linde[1] have presented scenarios in which our present universe was created out of a 'mother' universe, and so on from past eternity. These models are admittedly very speculative, but so are all models concerned with the early universe. Given the inflationary big-bang framework, it does not appear to be unduly implausible to conjecture that, if a universe can be created via a quantum fluctuation in empty space, further universes could be similarly created within the space of a previously existing universe.

We conclude that, although big-bang cosmology is often interpreted as implying that the physical universe has a finite past, a closer examination reveals a rather ambiguous situation. The argument for a finite past rests upon a particular interpretation of a dubious extrapolation beyond the known physical laws, to the exclusion of various beginningless alternatives that seem no less plausible. In short, even within big-bang cosmology, an eternal universe cannot be definitely ruled out. Moreover, near the singularity the definition of time is such that it is not clear – at least within big-bang cosmology – what is meant by the singularity being caused by a prior event.

The Second Law of Thermodynamics

In a previous chapter we described the second law of thermodynamics, which asserts that a closed system continually increases its entropy, or amount of disorder. As we noted, its application to the universe as a whole led to the conclusion that, at some finite time in the future, the universe would suffer a 'heat death', when there would be no more energy available to support life or do any useful work. It also implied that the world was initially wound up in a state of low entropy. For theists this was soon seen as evidence for a divine creation of the universe. A host of theists – including Zanstra[2] and

---

[1] Markov, 'Some Problems of Modern Theory of Gravitation', in *The Past and Future of the Universe,* Moscow: Nauka, 1989, pp. 11–23, and Linde, 'The Self-Reproducing Inflationary Universe', *Scientific American,* Nov. 1994, pp. 48–55.

[2] Herman Zanstra, 'Is Religion Refuted by Physics or Astronomy?', *Vistas in Astronomy,* 1968, *10,* pp. 1–21, and 'Thermodynamics, Statistical Mechanics, and the Universe', *ibid.,* pp. 23–44.

Craig – have pointed to the second law as one of the clearest indicators of a divine beginning of the physical world.

As an argument for the finite past of the universe, it has some advantages over the argument based on the big-bang singularity. As we saw in the previous sections, the latter is quite speculative and model-dependent. Moreover, big-bang cosmology may well be in vogue at the moment, but who knows what the future may bring? Perhaps big-bang cosmology will be dethroned by some other cosmology postulating an infinite past. The second law, on the contrary, is of such a fundamental nature that few would doubt its universal validity. It is quite widely conceded that the second law of thermodynamics is one of the most basic laws of all science.

In 1928 Sir Arthur Eddington and Sir James Jeans, the foremost English astronomers at that time, came to the conclusion that the universe must have been wound up at a finite time in the past and is now heading towards a heat death. As to whether this can be considered as scientific proof for a Creator, Eddington remarks:

> Scientists and theologians alike must regard as somewhat crude the naïve theological doctrine which (suitably disguised) is at present to be found in every textbook of thermodynamics, namely that some billions of years ago God wound up the material universe and has left it to chance ever since. This should be regarded as the working-hypothesis of thermodynamics rather than its declaration of faith. It is one of those conclusions from which we can see no logical escape – only it suffers from the drawback that it is incredible.[1]

Nevertheless, this argument for the finite past of the universe has its foes. It has been challenged at a number of points. First of all, although most contemporary cosmologists believe in the applicability of the second law to the universe as a whole, some doubts have been expressed regarding this. For example, Drees contends that an expanding universe is not really closed since entropy is carried away into expanding space by the background radiation. The expansion works as if there were an environment, although there is none.[2]

However, to this it may be replied that big-bang models assume the universe to be everywhere the same, so that as much radiation leaves

[1] Eddington, *The Internal Constitution of the Stars,* p. 84.
[2] Willem B. Drees, *Beyond the Big Bang: Quantum Cosmologies and God,* Th.D. thesis, Rijksuniversiteit Groningen, The Netherlands, 1989, p. 26.

each region (which may have expanding dimensions containing a fixed mass-energy) as enters it. For each such region a net entropy gain is thus to be expected.

Drees asserts that there exists no clear concept of entropy in relation to gravity, hence the application of the concept of entropy to the whole universe is questionable. Nevertheless, while the relation of entropy to gravity may not be quite as clear-cut as the situation in statistical non-gravitational systems, there is no reason for thinking that such a fundamental law as entropy gain should not apply. Penrose,[1] for example, has argued that entropy can be quite reasonably applied to gravitational structures.

Lerner, too, in advocating an infinite universe of ever-increasing complexity, denies the cosmic applicability of the second law. He claims that, contrary to the second law, the cosmos evolves from chaos to order:

> Conventional physics views any change as a necessary regression, as devolution toward equilibrium. Yet if we look at the longterm tendency of evolution, reality is just the opposite – the universe winds up, not down . . . The universe we observe is simply not decaying; the generalization of 'the law of increasing disorder' to the entire cosmos is unsupported by observation . . . If there is no tendency toward evolution or progress in nature, then human existence itself is nothing but a meaningless accident . . . in a timeless or a decaying cosmos there is no room for anything that has value for humanity, no room for consciousness, joy, sadness, or hope.[2]

Consequently, he contends that the second law holds only in systems that are already very close to equilibrium, where each part in the system has almost the same temperature and there is little useful energy left. If, however, the system were already far from equilibrium, with significant flows of energy through it then, Lerner affirms, it would not tend to return toward equilibrium but would move away from it, creating order and structure in the process.

Lerner's proposed mechanism is the growth of fluctuations through instability. He gives the example of the growth of convection patterns in a heated pot of water, where instability creates order by 'capturing' the flow of heat energy from the stove to the water.

[1] Penrose, 'Difficulties with Inflationary Cosmology', 1989.
[2] E. J. Lerner, *The Big Bang Never Happened*, New York: Times Books, 1991, pp. 287–91.

The trouble with this example is that an external energy flow, which is itself ordered, is needed to set off the growth of order in the heated water. Lerner has not shown that the total order of the entire system (water, pot, flame) has in fact been increased. Thus he has not demonstrated that the universe as a whole can escape the consequences of the second law.

Since there is, of course, no conclusive proof either way, a word of caution might be in order about drawing universal conclusions from the second law. Yet, if one follows the plausible principle that known physical laws should be followed as much as possible, rather than postulating new ones, then the evidence currently favours the universal applicability of the second law. Even so, it may still be possible to avoid a finite beginning or a heat-death future. It was suggested by the Austrian physicist Ludwig Boltzmann in the late nineteenth century that the order we see may be due just to random fluctuations. In a very large universe, even if it were in a state of thermal equilibrium, random motions would still produce small, highly ordered regions of lower entropy. If such regions are large enough and last long enough, then life might originate.

Is this feasible? It has been calculated by Zanstra that an appreciable entropy fluctuation can occur only in a volume containing just a few particles. Yet the entire visible universe seems to be in a state of low entropy. Can we really consider the entire visible universe as a random fluctuation? This implies not only that the universe must be vastly larger than the region now observable, but also that the unobserved portion of the universe, which is presumably in a chaotic state of high entropy, must be drastically different from the orderly universe observed. This is contrary to the usual assumption of uniformity.

Again, we come to the conclusion that the evidence favours a universe winding down from an initial state of high order. This initial state need not have occurred a *finite* time ago, however. In principle the entropy could have increased from a minimum value in the *infinite* past. This would be the case in a cosmological model such as Gamow's infinitely-old contraction-expansion universe, described above.

---

[1] Zanstra, *Thermodynamics*, p. 33.

Thus the second law of thermodynamics falls short of proving the beginning of the universe a finite time ago. Yet it may still be of value for one looking for signs of the Creator. For, if the second law is indeed applicable to the universe as a whole – which seems plausible – then the universe has been steadily unwinding. But how did it come to be wound up in the first place? Where did the initial order come from? Such questions lead us to a second proof for the existence of God: the argument from design.

To sum up, both the philosophical and scientific arguments for a beginning to the universe are flawed. The case against the existence of the actual infinite was found to be fallacious. The argument from the supposed big-bang singularity relies too much on a specific cosmological model and on speculative extrapolations beyond the model's range of validity. Although the case based on thermodynamics avoids these shortcomings, it, too, falls short of definitely proving that the universe began a finite time ago.

This is not to deny that cosmological evidence for a beginning seems plausible. But plausibility falls short of proof and, as we saw, those who wish to deny a beginning can construct beginningless alternatives which, in their eyes, may seem more credible. Hard observational evidence alone is insufficient to overcome the subjective nature of scientific theorizing.

Moreover, we have thus far restricted ourselves to a universe operating through purely natural causes. Dropping this restriction allows for the possibility of a supernatural being who has interacted with the universe from eternity, perhaps, for example, by adding useful energy from time to time. Hence we can know for certain whether or not the universe has a finite past only if God chose to reveal such information to us. Only on the basis of biblical teaching can we definitely conclude that the universe was indeed created a finite time ago.

The Argument from Design

The argument from design, too, has been a popular argument for the existence of God. It was strongly promoted by William Paley in his book *Natural Theology*, published at the end of the eighteenth century. In it he argued that the intricate organization of the world was strong evidence for the existence of an intelligent Creator, in much the same way as the detailed mechanism of a watch was due to the purposeful craftsmanship of a watchmaker.

The main question is whether the observed complexity of the universe necessarily involves a Creator, or whether the complexity could be explained as the end result of purely natural processes. A prime example concerns the amazing characteristics of biological organisms and systems. These were often taken as yielding the most persuasive evidence for a divine designer. This interpretation was challenged by Charles Darwin's *On the Origin of the Species* (1859), wherein he proposed that the observed biological diversity was caused solely by random mutations and natural selection.

A Fine-Tuned Universe

Recently a number of apologists have supported the argument from design by appeals to developments in cosmology. It seems that, from various cosmological considerations, the universe is remarkably fine-tuned. Had the physical laws and initial conditions been only slightly different, then, it seems, the universe would have been unable to sustain life. Much has been written about the spectacular fine-tuning of the universe for human life. We shall consider only a few typical factors.

1. Entropy

If entropy, the amount of disorder of the universe, is always increasing, then the universe must initially have been created in an orderly condition, as discussed in the previous section. According to Paul Davies:

> If the universe is simply an accident, the odds against it containing any appreciable order are ludicrously small. If the big bang was just a random event, then the probability seems overwhelming (a colossal understatement) that the emerging cosmic material would be in thermodynamic equilibrium at maximum entropy with zero order. As this was clearly not the case, it appears hard to escape the conclusion that the actual state of the universe had been 'chosen' or selected somehow from the huge number of available states, all but an infinitesimal fraction of which are totally disordered. And if such an exceedingly improbable initial state was selected, there surely had to be a selector or designer to 'choose' it?[1]

[1] *God and the New Physics,* New York: Simon & Schuster, 1983, p. 168.

2. The Expansion Rate

The expansion rate of the universe appears to be very critically balanced. Had it been a fraction less it would have recollapsed within seconds; had it been a fraction more, galaxy formation would have been impossible. To avoid these disasters the expansion rate during the early instants had to be fine-tuned to about one part in 10^{55}, according to John Leslie. The expansion rate can be accounted for by inflation, but this itself requires fine-tuning: two components of an expansion-driven cosmological constant cancel each other to an accuracy of one part in 10^{50}. Leslie[1] estimates that a change by one part in 10^{100} in the present strengths either of the nuclear weak force or of gravity might disastrously end this cancellation.

3. The Elements

Hydrogen and carbon are essential for life, at least for life as we know it. Had the nuclear weak force been a little stronger, the big bang would have burned all hydrogen to helium; had it been a little weaker, the neutrons formed at early times would not have decayed into protons, and again there would be no hydrogen. Leslie[2] notes that, for carbon to be created in quantity inside stars the strong nuclear force had to have its present value to within 1% either way.

4. Life

Fine-tuning is needed not only in the initial conditions and in the physical forces, but also in the generation of complexity, in particular life. Various estimates have been made for the chance occurrence of life. Barrow and Tipler[3] find the odds for assembling a single gene to be of the order of 10^{-109}. The odds against assembling by chance a human genome are found to be about $10^{-12000000}$, or 1 chance out of 1 followed by 12 million zeroes. From this extremely small probability they conclude that life, particularly human life, must be exceedingly rare in the universe. It should be noted that this calculation does not include the further long odds of finding favourable conditions on a favourable planet suitably placed near a favourable star.

These are just a few examples. Many similar phenomena are cited by Barrow and Tipler and Leslie. It appears that the universe is precisely geared to be receptive to intelligent life.

[1] *Universes,* London: Routledge, 1989, p. 3.   [2] *Ibid.,* p. 4.
[3] John D. Barrow and Frank J. Tipler, *The Anthropic Cosmological Principle,* Oxford: The University Press, 1986, p. 565.

A host of Christians, including John Leslie, Richard Swinburne and Hugh Ross, have based their case for the existence of God upon such cosmological evidence of design. They are not alone. Many non-Christian scientists, too, have been struck by the spectacular fine-tuning of the universe. Thus Stephen Hawking, as quoted by Boslough, states:

> The odds against a universe like ours emerging out of something like the big bang are enormous. I think there are clearly religious implications.[1]

Freeman Dyson, in a similar vein, writes of:

> . . . numerous accidents that seem to conspire to make our universe habitable . . . The more I examine the universe and the details of its architecture, the more evidence I find that the universe in some sense must have known we were coming.[2]

And also Paul Davies comes to the conclusion:

> It is hard to resist the impression that the present structure of the universe, apparently so sensitive to minor alterations in the numbers, has been rather carefully thought out.[3]

In a later work Davies comments that 'the impression of design is overwhelming'.[4]

Alternatives to Design

Yet such conclusions are by no means unanimous. Various alternative explanations of the apparent fine-tuning have been proposed, of which we shall examine the following:

1. *Many-World Theories* – in an infinity of universes everything is possible.
2. *Anthropic Principles* – had the universe been different we would not be here to see it.
3. *Theories of Everything* – a theory of everything will show that only one world is possible, that our world is not accidental but necessary.

[1] John Boslough, *Stephen Hawking's Universe,* New York: William Morrow, 1985, p. 121.
[2] Freeman Dyson, *Disturbing the Universe*, New York: Harper and Row, 1979, p. 250.
[3] *God and the New Physics,* New York: Simon and Schuster, 1983, p. 189.
[4] *The Cosmic Blueprint*, New York: Simon and Schuster, 1988, p. 203.

4. *Natural Selection* – our universe is the result of a natural selection process.

1. Many-World Theories

One way to explain the apparent design in this remarkable fine-tuning is to suggest the existence of a multiplicity of universes, existing either successively or simultaneously. If there were vastly many universes, with differing properties, then it would not be improbable if life arose on some of these. Our universe would then be one of those fortunate rare ones.

Various mechanisms for generating multiple universes have been proposed:

a. Successive cycles of an oscillating universe. If information is lost at a singularity, and if each new universe has different properties, as suggested by John Wheeler, and discussed previously, then a whole succession of different universes can be generated. Currently, however, with observational evidence favouring an open universe with no future cycles, this alternative is not feasible.

b. Multiple domains. If the universe is very large, perhaps even infinite, then it is possible that huge regions, effectively out of sight of each other, have different properties.

c. Many-worlds quantum theory. One interpretation of quantum mechanics is that, each time an observer makes a measurement, he, along with the universe, is split in two! Whenever a choice is to be made between the various possible outcomes of a quantum event, the universe branches off into a set of universes, one corresponding to each possible choice. This yields an infinity of parallel universes, virtually independent, with different properties.

d. Quantum vacuum fluctuations. If our universe could be created from nothing via a quantum vacuum fluctuation, as discussed in a previous section, there is nothing to prevent this happening innumerable times. Perhaps a 'baby' universe could in such a fashion be generated within our own universe.

In any one of these schemes the presence of our universe, with its relative hospitality towards life, is explained as a chance occurrence, a rare phenomena in the virtually infinite set of universes, the vast majority of which have been barren.

Swinburne contends that the many-worlds view goes against normal scientific method.[1] We extrapolate to distant parts of the universe by assuming that the present laws will hold. All the evidence points to the constancy of these laws. The most striking evidence of this comes from the observed isotropy of the universe. There may be states of affairs (for example, at a singularity) where some of the laws will not hold, but there is no evidence suggesting that in general the laws were different. In all regions of the space and time that are spatially and temporally related to our own, we have no reason to doubt that the physical laws and boundary conditions were quantitatively the same as our own; we have no reason to doubt the universal application of induction.

In the many-worlds quantum theory there are an infinity of universes, none of which will ever produce any observable effect on our universe. Swinburne reasons that it would be much simpler to interpret quantum mechanics indeterministically, as only describing physical probabilities of the behaviour of the real constituents of the universe, and to postulate that the boundary conditions do lie within a narrow range. According to Swinburne:

> It is a crucial tenet of the scientific method that entities are not to be postulated beyond necessity . . . to postulate infinitely many worlds in order to save a preferred interpretation of a formula, which is in no way obviously simpler than the alternative explanation, and to avoid having to postulate a very narrow range of boundary conditions, seems crazy.[2]

He concludes that it is much simpler to explain our tailor-made universe by specifying just one entity of a simple kind: God. Our life-producing world is more plausibly explained by the existence of God than by positing the existence of an infinity of unseen worlds.

John Leslie, too, has argued that the God hypothesis is simpler and more plausible as an explanation of the fine-tuning than these many-worlds hypotheses. According to Leslie,[3] the latter are all very artificial and unsupported by any independent evidence, whereas there exists other evidence in favour of belief in God. Also John Polkinghorne argues for the superiority of the theistic option:

[1] Richard Swinburne, 'Argument from the Fine-Tuning of the Universe', *in* John Leslie, *Physical Cosmology and Philosophy*, London, 1990, p. 167.
[2] *Ibid.*, p. 171.
[3] 'Modern Cosmology and the Creation of Life', *in* E. McMullin, *Evolution and Creation*, Notre Dame: The University Press, 1985.

A possible explanation of equal intellectual respectability – and to my mind greater economy and elegance – would be that this one world is the way it is because it is the creation of the will of a Creator who purposes that it should be so.[1]

On the other hand, Drees doubts that simplicity favours design over multiple worlds. Simplicity, he argues, has to do with the *structure* of a theory, not the number of *entities* it predicts.[2]

Could the two alternatives be combined? Ian Barbour thinks that one could interpret many-world hypotheses theistically, and that God and chance need not be mutually exclusive. He suggests the possibility that:

> God created many universes in order that life and thought would occur in this one. Admittedly, this gives chance an inordinately large role, and it involves a colossal waste and inefficiency if there are many lifeless universes. But then again, one might reply that for God neither space nor time is in short supply, so that efficiency is a dubious criterion.[3]

To this one might respond that, surely, an omniscient God has no need of chance. Indeed, to him there is no such thing as chance. He knows which initial conditions will generate favourable universes, hence why should he create countless many just to generate ours?

2. The Anthropic Principles

To explain the fine-tuning of our universe in a non-theistic fashion one needs not just a multiplicity of universes but also an observational selection effect. How is it that we just happen to be in a universe favourable to life? One obvious answer is that, if the universe had been different, we would not be here to observe it. Hence the physical properties we observe are the result of an all-embracing selection effect. To quote Barrow and Tipler:

> Any observed properties of the universe that may initially appear astonishingly improbable, can only be seen in their true perspective after we have accounted for the fact that certain properties of the universe are necessary prerequisites for the evolution and existence of observers at all.[4]

[1] *One World: The Interaction of Science and Theology*, Princeton: The University Press, 1986, p. 80.
[2] Drees, *Beyond the Big Bang*, p. 68.
[3] *Religion in an Age of Science*, San Francisco: Harper, 1990, p. 138.
[4] *The Anthropic Cosmological Principle*, p. 2.

Such an explanation makes use of what is called the *anthropic principle*. The anthropic principle is used in various forms:

a. The Weak Anthropic Principle (WAP). This is the most basic version of the anthropic principle. It refers primarily to the self-selection principle: what we observe must be compatible with our existence. The definition given by Barrow and Tipler is:

> The observed values of all physical constants . . . take on values restricted by the requirement that there exist sites where carbon-based life can evolve and by the requirement that the universe be old enough for it to have already done so.[1]

In short, our observations must be biased in favour of scenarios in which we exist. This is the weakest form of the anthropic principle.

b. The Strong Anthropic Principle (SAP). This is more stringent and much more speculative. Barrow and Tipler define it as the concept that 'the universe must have those properties which allow life to develop within it at some stage in its history'.[2] It is often tied in with the multiple-worlds view: that all possibilities must occur, including a few where life arises.

Whereas the weak form states that the universe has to be such that life *can* occur, the strong form specifies that life *must* occur. The SAP specifies that life must arise, not just in our universe, but in all possible universes. Swinburne notes that the WAP is just a trivial truth: any theory must be compatible with the observations.[3] It must be kept in mind that the WAP is not a causal explanation: we cannot say that the initial conditions and laws are the consequence of our existence. Rather, it is the other way around. As to the SAP, with its claim that the laws of nature must be such that life can exist, this has no evidence to support it. According to current knowledge, the opposite seems to be true. The universe was very much more likely *not* to produce life.

Heinz Pagels asserts that the anthropic principle is much ado about nothing, being deeply flawed and having no place in cosmology.[4] He complains that it is entirely *ad hoc*, predicts nothing, and is immune from experimental falsification. It has been more fruitful, he argues,

---

[1] *Ibid.*, p. 16.   [2] *Ibid.*, p. 21.
[3] 'Argument from the Fine-Tuning of the Universe', p. 165.
[4] 'A Cozy Cosmology', *in* Leslie, *Physical Cosmology and Philosophy*, p. 175.

to search for explanations in terms of the laws of nature than to point to an alleged selection effect. The question boils down to whether the initial conditions of the universe were arbitrary or necessary. Only in the former case does it make sense to appeal to a selection effect such as the anthropic principle. Until the origin of the universe is better understood, it is premature to invoke the anthropic principle. The anthropic principle, Pagels contends, detracts from real science; those who use it have in effect given up on the attempt to find a truly fundamental explanation for the nature of things. He notes that the anthropic principle is in direct competition with the theistic principle: that the universe seems fine-tuned for our existence because it was fine-tuned for our existence by God. His assessment of those upholding the anthropic principle is:

> Of course, some scientists, believing science and religion mutually exclusive, find this idea unattractive. Faced with questions that do not neatly fit into the framework of science, they are loath to resort to religious explanation; yet their curiosity will not let them leave matters unaddressed. Hence, the anthropic principle. It is the closest that some atheists can get to God.

The WAP may explain something if combined with a multiple universe theory. But it does not explain why we have precisely this universe and not one, say, slightly less isotropic. If this universe is the way it is only for the purpose of creating life, then its arrangement could have been much less precise.

3. The Theory of Everything

The above comments by Pagels raise a third possibility: that the apparently arbitrary value of the physical constants are in fact dictated by a more basic law. It may be that a more fundamental theory will show that the constants *must* have the values that they have. In that case coincidences such as thus listed above will turn out to be necessities.

Recently efforts have been made to construct a Grand Unified Theory, which would unite the nuclear and electromagnetic forces into a single theory. Much work has gone also into attempting to combine general relativity and quantum mechanics into a unified theory of quantum gravity. Such a theory is needed in situations where the matter-energy density is extremely high, such as is envisioned shortly after the big bang. The latest theories, involving multi-dimensional 'superstrings', try to fuse all of these forces into a single theory, a Theory of Everything (TOE). It is called a theory of *everything* because it is thought that everything in the universe could be logically deduced from such a theory.

A successful TOE might seem to undermine the argument from design. However, according to Barbour,[1] such a theory would be welcomed by the theist as part of God's design. While such a theory might show that only one universe is possible and that the characteristics of our universe are necessary rather than accidental, it would still leave unexplained why or how it came to be instantiated in the real world.

However, even a TOE would not totally explain fine-tuning. To derive conclusions about particulars we need not only universal laws, but also appropriate boundary conditions. As Barbour asserts, 'Evolution must be described by a historical account of events and not by predictive laws alone'.[2] Thus we would still be left with the question as to why the boundary conditions were such as they were.

Further, for a TOE to explain literally everything, including the characteristics not only of particular species, but also of particular individuals, clearly requires such a detailed knowledge of the boundary conditions so as to be practically impossible for humans to acquire.

Stephen Hawking has also considered the possibility of a TOE. He finds that even if such a theory could be found, it would still leave unanswered questions:

> Even if there is only one possible unified theory, it is just a set of rules and equations. What is it that breathes fire into the equations and makes a universe for them to describe? The usual approach of science of constructing a mathematical model cannot answer the questions of why there should be a universe for the model to describe.[3]

But Hawking is optimistic:

> However, if we discover a complete theory, it should in time be understandable . . . by everyone . . . Then we shall all . . . be able to take part in the discussion of why it is that we and the universe exist. If we find

[1] *Religion in an Age of Science*, p. 139.   [2] *Ibid.*, p. 139.
[3] S. W. Hawking, *A Brief History of Time*, New York: Bantam, 1988, p. 174.

the answer to that, it would be the ultimate triumph of human reason –
for then we would know the mind of God.[1]

Hawking overestimates the value of a TOE, while underestimating
the content of God's mind.

In summary, even if a TOE could be established, the question of
design still remains. One still needs to explain the boundary conditions, the existence of the TOE, and that of the universe itself. All of
this assumes, of course, that everything in the universe is the result of
normal, physical laws. Allowance for spiritual influences and
miracles diminishes even further the significance of a TOE.

4. A Naturally Selected Universe

The American astronomer Edward Harrison has proposed that our
universe was made by highly intelligent forms of life living in another
universe and that the apparent fine-tuning in our universe has been
naturally selected.[2] He contends that it may be possible to create a
universe, under controlled laboratory conditions, by forming a small
(10 kg), black hole from high-energy particles. The physical constants in the offspring universe would probably be much the same as
the values in the parent universe.

Highly intelligent beings could then create new universes that
would be hospitable for intelligent life. Only universes containing
intelligent beings are likely to reproduce.

He assumes that, initially, there was a set of universes, with differing fundamental constants, containing at least one universe where
intelligent life occurred. Thereafter, by reproduction, intelligent universes dominate the set. Universes most hospitable to intelligent life
are naturally selected by their ability to reproduce.

Harrison argues that belief in a supernatural creator terminates
scientific inquiry, whereas the anthropic principle implies a vast
wasteland of mostly barren universes. His option, on the other hand,
has life itself taking over the creation business, which then drops out
of the religious sphere and becomes a subject open to scientific
investigation.

[1] *Ibid.*, p. 175.
[2] 'The Natural Selection of Universes Containing Intelligent Life', *Quarterly
Journal of the Royal Astronomical Society*, 1995, 36, pp. 193–203.

It is clear, however, that this proposal has a number of weaknesses.[1] First, the proposed scenario of universe creation is, to say the least, highly speculative, based on cosmological conceptions and particle physics theories that have not been empirically tested. To the extent that it postulates a parent universe no longer spatially or causally connected to our own, it is inherently unverifiable.

Second, natural selection, as an explanation of complexity, generally involves an evolution in the direction of increased complexity. Here, however, the direction is reversed: our universe is postulated to have been created by superior, rather than inferior, beings. Using Paley's analogy, this is much like finding a watch and inferring from it, not a watchmaker, but a sophisticated watch-making machine.

It explains the original problem at the high expense of replacing it with a much more difficult one. We are still left with the question as to what created the initial set of universes, particularly the one containing the superior intelligent beings. This brings us back to many-world theories and anthropic principles.

In short, the proposal that our universe was created by intelligent beings in a parent universe is not a viable explanation of the origin of our universe. The natural selection scenario is contrived, unverifiable, and ultimately reduces merely to an unnecessarily more elaborate version of the theistic or anthropic principles. It seems more rational to consider our universe as the first one to contain created intelligent beings.

Summing up, the observed features of the universe seem to be much more plausibly explained through divine design than by the alternative explanations of many-world theories, anthropic principles, theories of everything, or natural selection. That, at least, is my personal assessment. Unfortunately, however, it must be granted that the argument lacks compulsion. In judging scientific theories, criteria such as simplicity and plausibility are often in the eye of the beholder, a beholder whose assessment is shaped by his deepest religious convictions.

---

[1] John Byl, 'On the Natural Selection of Universes', *Quarterly Journal of the Royal Astronomical Society*, 1996, 37, pp. 369–71.

Design and Evolution

If the universe did in fact have just the right parameters needed to evolve to its present state, with all its detailed structure and diverse forms of life, this might be seen as strong evidence for evolution. After all, in a universe created instantaneously, in mature form, cosmological parameters, such as the density and expansion rate, could conceivably have been much different. It may seem that, from a creationist perspective, the fine-tuning is inexplicable, merely coincidental.

In response, we note first that much of the fine-tuning allegedly needed for life to evolve is needed also to sustain life. Life – at least in the form we know it – depends critically on the unique properties of the elements carbon, nitrogen, hydrogen and oxygen. The necessary life-sustaining properties would no longer exist if, for example, the nuclear or electron-magnetic forces were only slightly different, or if the relative masses of electrons and neutrons were in slightly different proportions. Thus also a recently created universe would require a considerable degree of fine-tuning of physical constants and laws.

A second factor is that many of so-called anthropic coincidences are based more on theoretical speculation than on observational fact. Take, for example, the high precision required of the early expansion rate, as listed above. Such a high precision is certainly not observed, the present expansion rate being known to a precision of no better than about 10 per cent. Rather, it is inferred purely on the basis of theoretical calculations. As such, the hypothetical fine-tuning could be viewed as a measure of the implausibility of big-bang cosmology, which can explain the present universe only on the basis of a conjectured but extremely improbable past expansion rate.

Conclusions

The time has come to wind up our discussion of the proofs for the existence of God. There are three points that I would like to stress:

1. Limitations of the Proofs

As we have seen, while various cosmological considerations may lead one to infer that the physical universe had a beginning at a finite time in the past, such a conclusion is by no means rigorous. There exists sufficient uncertainty regarding physical laws and their application that other possibilities cannot be conclusively eliminated. The same general considerations apply to the argument from design. Here, too, other options might be able to account for the occurrence of apparent design.

Nevertheless, while such arguments are not compelling, they clearly do have some persuasive force. Indeed, a number of astronomers have drawn theistic implications from big-bang cosmology. This has led some to reject big-bang cosmology and others to accept a variety of different conceptions of God.

Few, however, seem to have thereby been converted to orthodox Christianity. Why is this the case? Possibly because the cosmological argument in itself leads only to a Prime Mover, an eternal being who initiates the universe. The teleological argument gets us little further. John Leslie, an advocate of the argument from design, contends that God need not be a person at all, but merely a 'creatively effective ethical requirement for the existence of a (good) universe or universes'.[1] These gods, impersonal abstractions as they are, are hardly objects inspiring or requiring our worship. At most this brings us only to a deistic God. The plausibility of providence, supernatural revelation and miracles must still be shown. Clearly, a huge step is still required to move beyond the Prime Mover or Designer, as suggested by the cosmological and teleological arguments, to the living God of the Bible.

2. Commitment to the Big Bang

A further problem in arguing from the big bang to the biblical God is the commitment to big-bang cosmology that it entails. Tying a theistic proof too closely to a particular model invites theological disaster should that model be dethroned. Even more important is the fact that the biblical view of reality is, as we shall show in a subsequent chapter, quite different from that of big-bang cosmology. These differences involve not only matters of origins and eschatology, but also the present structure of the universe. For example, big-bang cosmology has no place for a transcendent God, for supernatural causes, or for an immortal soul.

---

[1] Leslie, *Universes*, p. 186.

Thus, in constructing a Christian view of reality, big-bang cosmology must ultimately be replaced by cosmological concepts that are more in accord with biblical givens. It follows that the argumentation of such apologists as Craig and Ross has limited value as a means to bolster the faith of Christians. Indeed, their endorsement of big-bang cosmology ushers in a new epistemology that gives much too high a weight to speculative theorizing, under the guise of general revelation. This will inevitably have grave implications for traditional views of biblical authority and hermeneutics.

Once we allow for a supernatural God, the case for a big-bang singularity is weakened, since other plausible options are now possible. If God could create the entire universe *ex nihilo* at the singularity, one could conjecture that, for example, he formed this universe out of a previous universe, or that he created the entire universe *ex nihilo* in the more recent past. The question now becomes a theological one and can be answered only through what God has revealed to us in his written Word.

3. The Role of General Revelation

Here one might ask: what about God's general revelation? Does God not reveal truths, such as big-bang cosmology, to us through nature?

According to Ross, the creation reveals not only essential truths about God's character, but also all the necessary steps to develop a right relationship with God.[1] These steps are uniquely corroborated by the Bible. As an illustration of the accessibility of this information, Ross asserts that Job, without the aid of Scripture, discerned all the elements of how man can find eternal life with God.

Whether Job did in fact attain such knowledge solely by brute observation and reason is, however, doubtful. One can not rule out the possibility that this knowledge was acquired from oral tradition (for example, from the patriarchs) or directly from God (see *Job* 38–41). The fact that Job's insights were disputed by his friends illustrates the fact that this knowledge, if revealed by creation, was certainly not perceived by others in the same way.

---

[1] Ross, *The Fingerprint of God*, p. 182.

While the Bible does assert that God reveals truth through nature, such truth is of a limited kind, concerning his nature:

> For the invisible things of him from the creation of the world are clearly seen, being understood by the things that are made, even his eternal power and Godhead; so that they are without excuse (*Rom.* 1:20).

The revelation of God through his works is primarily a matter of God's *self*-revelation. As such it is apprehended, first of all, not through scientific investigation but through faith. This is evident in the Psalms (for example, Psalms 33 and 104), which reveal the insight of faith into the work of God's hands. The nature-psalms deal not with *abstract* aspects of cosmic reality but rather with *naïve* (in the good sense of the word) reality. Even pre-scientific man could discern the order, beauty, vastness, and harmony of the creation.

God reveals himself through nature in such a way that every man is aware of the true God. This knowledge does not depend upon logical proof or scientific argumentation. It is much more direct. Man, made in the image of God, cannot look upon the things of nature without immediately perceiving them as the work of God. Look at the majesty, beauty, goodness and order around us: at the stars, flowers and so on. Is it not obvious that they must have been created by a great God?

Yet while the divinity of God is clearly revealed through nature, man distorts and suppresses this knowledge; man rejects God and becomes futile in his thinking, his senseless mind is darkened. Therefore God gives him up to dishonourable passions and a base mind (see *Rom.*1:18, 21–32).

It is now only through the preaching of the gospel and the operation of the Holy Spirit that man can come to a proper knowledge of God. Fallen man needs Scripture to interpret nature correctly. Thus, while there is a natural revelation, this does not lead to a natural theology: without Scripture to guide us man loses himself in futile speculations. To use Calvin's analogy, man's eyes are too dim to read the book of nature properly; we need the spectacles of Scripture to dispel the darkness and give us a clear view of the true God, thus correcting our confused notions of Deity.[1]

---

[1] John Calvin, *Institutes of the Christian Religion,* 1559, I. vi. 1.

As noted by Stephen Spencer, the nature Psalms (for example, Psalms 8, 19, 29, 65 and 104) do not provide a basis for natural theology. The Psalms are set in the midst of the people of God. Here nature is never seen as a revelation independent of God's Word: God's law is never far from the psalmist's thoughts. What we have here is a *theology of nature* rather than a *natural theology*. God's natural revelation is interpreted within the framework of his Word rather than independent of it.

It must be stressed that the knowledge revealed through nature concerns only God's attributes and that this knowledge is acquired through our direct experience of nature, not through our scientific models. There is no biblical evidence suggesting that God reveals himself through fallible human theorizing. Indeed, the Bible stresses the limitations of human knowledge, particularly with regard to origins (see, for example, *Job* 38-41; *Isa.* 41:21–24; *Eccles.* 3:11). Big-bang cosmology, to the extent that it consists of theoretical extrapolations beyond the observational data, cannot be considered as part of God's general revelation. It is not a revealed truth. It is mere speculation and as such does not count as valid evidence for God. Nor is it needed: man is already without excuse.

In short, cosmology tells us very little about God. Through a study of the structure and properties of the universe we may gain a better understanding of God's handiwork, but not a great deal about the Creator. The scope of natural theology – the study of God via nature and human reason, as opposed to revelation – is extremely limited.

What is left, then, of the apologetic status of these theistic proofs? Although they fall short of definitely proving the existence of God – particularly the God of the Bible – their prime value consists in showing that the naturalism inherent in modern science cannot plausibly be maintained indefinitely. Ultimately, naturalism fails to provide satisfactory explanations for the full richness of our experienced reality and gives little insight into the deeper questions of origins, purpose and destiny. Naturalism, consistently applied, undermines itself.

[1] S. R. Spencer, 'Is Natural Theology Biblical?', *Grace Theological Journal*, 1988, 9, pp. 59–72.

5

Cosmology, Life and the Future

Thus far we have concentrated primarily on issues involving the past and present structure of the cosmos. Yet the future of the universe is also of great interest. What does modern cosmology have to tell us regarding the future?

In the immediate future, one of the hopes of today's society is to establish contact with extra-terrestrial civilizations. We shall thus first examine the likelihood and implications of such an event. But what about the more distant future? Can we expect human life, or for that matter, life in any form, to continue to exist indefinitely? Most cosmologists are rather pessimistic about this but, as we shall see, there are at least a few who have sketched more optimistic scenarios.

Finally, of prime importance to us as individual persons, is the question of our own immortality. Even if life were to continue forever, this can be of only limited comfort to the individual who faces death and extinction. Does science offer us any hope for life after death?

Life in the Universe

Is the earth the only cradle of life in the universe? Is man alone? Or are there intelligent extra-terrestrial beings (other than spiritual beings such as angels and demons) somewhere in outer space? Many people believe that such creatures do exist and that life is widespread throughout the universe. In 1992 the U.S. space agency NASA launched a major project called SETI (Search for Extra-Terrestrial Intelligence). This uses radio telescopes around the world to examine distant stars for signals that might be of artificial origin. Thus far the results have been completely negative. Nevertheless, it is useful to examine the case for extra-terrestrial life and intelligence, taking into account both scientific and theological considerations.

A Brief History of ETI

Speculations about the possibility of extra-terrestrial life (ETL) and intelligence (ETI) have a long history.[1] They can be traced back at least to the Greek philosopher Democritus (c. 460–370 BC), who believed that there were an infinite number of worlds, each with a central, inhabited planet. He was also convinced that the moon was populated. However, belief in ETI was not widespread in ancient times; nor, for that matter, in the medieval world, whose finite, hierarchical cosmology had no place for other inhabited planets, although the existence of legions of angels – and demons – was acknowledged.

The big boost for ETI came with the advent of the Copernican revolution in the sixteenth century. With the demotion of the earth to just another planet, there was no longer any reason to believe that it was unique in either composition or function. Thus, for example, the astronomer Johannes Kepler, among many others, thought that the sun, the planets, and particularly the moon, were also populated.

By the end of the eighteenth century, belief in ETI was very widespread in the scientific community. The demonstration of the absence of a lunar atmosphere had by this time ruled out the possibility of lunar intelligence. But this merely transported the presumed presence of ETI to other celestial objects. The famous philosopher Immanuel Kant[2] wrote a treatise describing in some detail the various life forms allegedly inhabiting the planets of our solar system. For a long time the prime candidate for ETI was Mars. Interest peaked in the early twentieth century when astronomer Percival Lowell announced that he had actually observed canals on Mars. However, such extravagant

---

[1] In what follows I have made use of the fine surveys of S. J. Dick (*Plurality of Worlds*, Cambridge University Press, 1981), and F. J. Tipler ('A Brief History of the ETI Concept', *Quarterly Journal of the Royal Astronomical Society*, 1982, 22, pp. 133–45).

[2] An English translation of Kant's *Allgemeine Naturgeschichte und Theorie des Himmels* (1755) by Stanley L. Jaki can be found in W. Yourgrau and A. D. Beck (eds.), *Cosmology, History, and Theology*, New York: Plenum Press, 1977, pp. 387–403.

claims were soon discounted by most professional astronomers, who failed to discern these observational features. Since then the search for ETI has abandoned the solar system in favour of the nearby stars. It is hoped that, in the near future, more sensitive radio telescopes will be able to detect evidence of advanced celestial civilizations.

The Scientific Case for ETI

How strong is the scientific case for ETI? Estimates vary considerably. During the last few years, there has been a lively debate between scientists who believe the existence of ETI to be widespread and those who think it to be very rare, with man perhaps being unique.

The optimists assert that many stars have planets, that a good fraction of those planets are suitable for life, that life will in fact develop on a sizeable proportion of such inhabitable planets, and, finally, that a significant number of these life-bearing planets will produce intelligent societies. Even if the fraction in each step is on the small side (say, 1 out of 100), the huge number of stars in our galaxy alone, estimated at about 300 billion, would still leave us with a potential of approximately three thousand intelligent civilizations in our galaxy. The chances are that many of these are much more advanced than us.

The pessimists, on the other hand, point out that all of the above factors are highly uncertain, that attaching numbers to them is no more than guessing, and that, in fact, some of the required steps in the chain seem to be extremely unlikely – if not impossible – on the basis of current scientific knowledge. Let us examine some of the more important links in the chain.

1. Habitable Planets

How many stars have planets? No one knows. Planets around other stars would be too faint to be observed directly by an earth-based telescope. Therefore the techniques for detecting them must be indirect. The prime method is to search for wobbles, caused by the gravitational attraction of the planet, in the motion of a star. From time to time such wobbles had been reported, and corresponding planetary systems deduced from them. Until recently, all such reports turned out to be false alarms, with 'wobbles' due to observational problems. In the last few years, however, the situation has changed. Glanz[1]

[1] James Glanz, 'Worlds Around Other Stars Shake Planet Birth Theory', *Science*, 1997, 276, pp. 1336–9.

reports that at least nine planets have been discovered. Although these planets are associated with sun-like stars, they are all of a huge, Jupiter-like size, and much closer to their star than had been predicted by standard theories of planet formation. They would certainly not support presently-known forms of life. Nevertheless, their discovery renders more plausible the possible existence of smaller, earth-like planets, which are less likely to cause observable wobbles in the parent star, and hence remain invisible to us.

2. Life By Chance

It is still a huge step from habitable planets to the actual formation of life on a planet. Thus far no life has been found by any space probes to the planets in our solar system. Until recently it was widely believed that Mars might harbour, if not canal-builders, at least some more primitive form of life. This hope was ruled out by tests by the Viking spacecraft, which landed on Mars in 1976, although some scientists still insist that the results were inconclusive.

Another means of searching for ETL is by examining extra-terrestrial rocks for signs of primitive life forms. Moon rock returned by the Apollo astronauts yielded no evidence for life. Much excitement was generated in August 1996, when NASA scientists announced the discovery of what they believed was evidence for primitive life on Mars.[1] A meteorite found in Antarctica, and thought to have come from Mars, contained microscopic carbonate globules that resembled bacteria found on earth. Unfortunately, it has since been determined that these globules could be due to other, inanimate, causes. Even if definite signs of life had been found, and even if it could be shown that these originated before the meteorite reached the earth, the result would be inconclusive. It was thought that an asteroid striking Mars could displace material into space, some of which, like the meteorite in question, might fall to earth. But if life can be transplanted from Mars to earth via an asteroid impact, the same mechanism could have brought life from earth to Mars. Hence an independent source of life on Mars would still be unproven.

How likely is it, from a naturalistic, evolutionary perspective, for life to evolve from non-life? Many complicated molecules have been

---

[1] D. S. MacKay et al., 'Search for Past Life on Mars: Possible Relic Biogenic Activity in Martian Meteorite ALH84001', *Science,* 1996, 273, pp. 924–30.

observed in interstellar space. These include water, methane, ammonia, methyl and ethyl alcohol and formic acid. It has been found that exposing a mixture of water vapour, methane and ammonia to ultraviolet light can lead to the formation of amino acids. Traces of amino acids have been found in some meteorites. Thus it is likely that amino acids are fairly numerous in the universe. The difficulty is getting beyond these to actual life.

Terrestrial organisms consist of two types of molecules, whose interaction results in life. The first are proteins, which make up the organism. The second are nucleic acids, such as DNA, which provide information for the structure of the organism and the means to pass on this information in reproduction. Proteins consist of amino acids; DNA consists of very long strands of bases. Both are composed of very intricate combinations of carbon, hydrogen, oxygen, nitrogen and a few other common atoms.

Granted the existence of the required amino acids and bases, it is quite another matter for these to combine randomly in just the right manner so as to form a complete cell. The probability of this occurring by chance is virtually zero. Fred Hoyle finds it so improbable that life on earth could have evolved by chance that he postulates that life arose in vast interstellar gas clouds.[1] Most evolutionary biologists consider the emergence of life from non-life to be immensely improbable and have generally been sceptical of the possibility of ETI. One estimate of the probability of life occurring by chance on an inhabitable planet, in the most favourable conditions, puts it as less than 10^{-32} (that is, one out of a hundred million trillion).[2] Paul Davies estimates the odds against random permutations of molecules assembling DNA as about 10^{4000} to one against! This is about the same as tossing a coin and getting heads 130,000 times in a row. At that rate he concludes that, over ten billion years, we would not expect to find another DNA molecule in the observable universe.[3]

[1] F. Hoyle, *The Intelligent Universe,* New York: Holt, Rinehart and Winston, 1983.
[2] M. H. Hart, *Extraterrestrials – Where are They?,* New York: Pergamon Press, 1982, p. 23.
[3] *Are We Alone: Philosophical Implications of the Discovery of Extraterrestrial Life,* New York: Basic Books, 1995, p. 28.

3. Higher Forms of Life

Another bottleneck occurs when moving from single-celled organisms to more advanced forms of life. According to Crawford, single-cell organisms appeared one billion years after the earth was formed, whereas it took over three billion years for multicellular animal life to evolve.[1] Furthermore, the evolution of multicellular animals from single-celled organisms allegedly occurred only once in history. He concludes that the evolution of complex life is therefore a lot more difficult than the initial development of life itself.

A further concern raised by Crawford is the emergence of intelligence. Many thousands of species, supposedly evolving over many millions of years, have resulted in only one sufficiently intelligent to develop technology and culture. This implies that, even given the existence of multi-cellular life, the evolutionary emergence of intelligence is very unlikely.

4. Self-Organizing Matter

Such pessimistic estimates have in turn been challenged by the optimists, who claim that our present grasp of the evolutionary mechanism is incomplete. They hope that further developments will vindicate their belief that evolution is much more probable than currently believed. After all, they ask, if life has evolved here, on this insignificant planet, why not elsewhere as well?

Paul Davies argues that the origin of life was not a miracle, nor a stupendously improbable accident, but rather the inevitable outworking of 'self-organizing' properties of matter.[2] He considers both life and consciousness to be fundamental 'emergent' properties of nature, natural consequences of the laws of physics which emerge in a physical system once it reaches a certain level of complexity. As such, he believes that life should be plentiful throughout the universe.

Unfortunately, Davies provides no details of how the necessary complexity can be reached, what the actual conditions for life and consciousness to 'emerge' are, or what are the physical laws which make such emergence inevitable. A further weakness of this position

---

[1] Ian Crawford, 'Galactic Civilizations: A Reply', *Astronomy & Geophysics,* 1997, 38 (Issue 6), p. 19.
[2] *Are We Alone.*

is that there is absolutely no scientific evidence to support it. Why have such 'self-organizing' properties not been observed to function in any of the many scientific experiments that have sought to synthesize life? Why, in the evolutionary view, did life on earth apparently originate only once? Davies' mysterious 'emergent properties' seem highly magical: stupendous miracles that are all the more inexplicable in that they allegedly occur purely by themselves, without any need for a divine intervention. This is little more than wishful thinking.

5. Where Are They?

Another argument for the scarcity of ETI is the fact that our earth has, apparently, not been colonized by extra-terrestrials (ETs). If ETI were common in our galaxy, then it might be thought that at least one of the more advanced civilizations would have explored and colonized the galaxy by now. Since we do not see ETs, and since there is no evidence that they have ever visited us (very few astronomers believe that UFOs are ET visitors!), it follows that ETI must be rare. The optimists have responded that perhaps these civilizations have no desire to colonize, or that perhaps they are keeping the earth as a nature preserve – a sort of cosmic zoo. Such options are rejected by the pessimists as being too implausible.

Motivation for Belief in ETI

Given the lack of scientific evidence for ETI, it is apparent that belief in ETI must rest on other, more philosophical considerations. Frank Tipler, who believes that we are alone in the universe, sees a strong similarity between belief in ETI and belief in UFOs:

> In fact, I suspect the psychological motivation of both beliefs to be the same, namely, the expectation that we are going to be saved from ourselves by some miraculous interstellar intervention.[1]

He supports this conclusion by citations from numerous prominent supporters of ETI. Typical is the following statement from Carl Sagan:

> The translation of a radio message from the depths of space . . . holds the greatest promise of both practical and philosophical benefits. In

[1] 'ETI Beings Do Not Exist', *Quarterly Journal of the Royal Astronomical Society*, 1980, *21*, p. 278.

particular, it is possible that among the first contents of such a message may be detailed descriptions for the avoidance of technological disaster, for a passage through adolescence to maturity.[1]

In a similar vein, Harvard astrophysicist A. G. W. Cameron writes:

If we can . . . communicate with some of these [advanced ET] societies, then we can expect to obtain an enormous enrichment of all phases of our sciences and arts. Perhaps we shall also receive valuable lessons in the techniques of stable world government.[2]

More recently, Paul Davies comments:

The interest in SETI among the general public stems in part, I maintain, from the need to find a wider context to their lives than this earthly existence provides. In an era when conventional religion is in sharp decline, the belief in super-advanced aliens . . . can provide some measure of comfort and inspiration . . . This sense of a religious quest may well extend to the scientists themselves, even though most of them are self-professed atheists.[3]

It is ironic that man, having rejected God, still searches the heavens for his salvation.

Theological Considerations

The above arguments are all based upon the premise that man, and life in general, had an evolutionary origin. Before Darwin most of the ETI arguments were formulated in creationist terms. How does the case for ETI look if one assumes a direct creative origin of life and intelligence?

In the seventeenth century the newly invented telescope revealed many hitherto invisible stars. Since these could hardly serve as light-bearers for man, their purpose became the object of debate. Many contended that they functioned as suns for other intelligent beings, placed there by God. Furthermore, it was argued that, since two universes are better than one, and since the wise Creator always chose the best, there should be an infinite number of inhabited worlds. Anything less was considered unworthy of an infinite Creator.

---

[1] Carl Sagan, *Broca's Brain*, New York: Random House, 1979, p. 276.
[2] *Interstellar Communication*, New York: Benjamin, 1963, p. 1. [3] *Are We Alone.*

We note in passing that, to creationists who believe the earth to be young, the lack-of-colonization objection to ETI is no longer valid, for then ETs would have had little time to develop and apply their exploration potential. On the other hand, the same consideration makes it extremely unlikely that, if civilizations similar to our own existed, we would be able to observe them, let alone interact with them, in the near future.

1. The Absence of Biblical Evidence for ETI

A number of theological objections have been raised against the belief in ETI. First, if ETs exist, why are they not mentioned in Scripture? The Lutheran theologian Philip Melanchthon (1497–1560) noted that, after God had created the earth, sun, moon, and stars of our cosmos, he rested and created nothing more, least of all another cosmos. Melanchthon pointed out that Scripture nowhere mentions the creation of man or other life outside of the earth (except, of course, the angels).

To this it was countered that the biblical account is directed towards man and his relationship to God. God may well have created other beings, of whose existence he did not deem it necessary to inform us.

2. Christ's Incarnation and ETI

The foremost theological objection to ETI has, however, always centred on the uniqueness of Christ's incarnation. This dates back at least to the Church Father Augustine (354–430). Augustine was concerned with opposing the cyclical view of history – the notion that history repeats itself in an endless cycle – current in his day. On the basis of such biblical texts as 'Christ also hath once suffered for sins' (*1 Pet.* 3:18) and 'Christ being raised from the dead dieth no more . . . he died unto sin once' (*Rom.* 6:9–10), he concluded in *The City of God* (xii.14) that the historical process of creation, fall and redemption could occur but once. This argument was extended by Albertus Magnus (1206–80) to refute also the idea of a multitude of worlds in space, rather than time. Melanchthon, too, in his rejection of ETI, contended that Christ could die only once and that men in other worlds could be saved only through knowledge of Christ.

The question of the uniqueness of Christ's sacrifice does not appear to bother most modern liberal theologians who discuss ETI. The acceptance of an evolutionary origin of man, and the corresponding rejection of the historicity of Adam and his Fall, opens the possibility that man's history could well be essentially repeated elsewhere. Paul Tillich and Dean Inge, for example, both suggest that the incarnation of Christ is not unique and could occur also on other planets.

The cosmologist E. A. Milne resolved the paradox between the uniqueness of Christ and the plurality of worlds by proposing that knowledge of the incarnation on earth could be transmitted to other planets via radio signals.[1] On this he was criticized by the theologian E. L. Mascall, who contended that salvation is not dependent upon our knowledge of Christ's incarnation. On the other hand, Mascall doubted that Christ's having been made man would suffice to make him the Saviour also of other, extraterrestrial beings. He suggested that the incarnation could be repeated on other planets.[2]

Recently John J. Davis[3] argues that the Christology of Colossians 1:15–20 is sufficiently vast in scope to provide a basis for the redemption of fallen beings anywhere in the universe, without the need for any additional incarnations or atonements. Referring to the *Westminster Confession of Faith* (VIII: 5,6), where the redemptive benefits of the death of Christ are said not to be limited by time, but to apply to the elect of all ages, Davis remarks:

> If the atonement can be understood as not being limited in time, it can just as readily be understood as not limited by space or distance. Christ assumed in the incarnation a true and complete human nature that he might represent man as the covenant head of a redeemed people. By extension, it could be postulated that the human nature of *Homo sapiens* could be designated by God to represent the nature of all sentient, embodied beings.

I do not find this notion very compelling. An atonement unlimited in time, applying to all the elect offspring of Adam, is quite distinct from an atonement applying to all, unrelated, intelligent beings throughout space. It is clear from Scripture that there exists a necessary connection between the first Adam and the second Adam,

[1] *Modern Cosmology and the Christian Idea of God,* Oxford: Clarendon Press, 1952.

[2] *Christian Theology and Natural Science*, London: Longmans, 1956.

[3] J. J. Davis, 'Search for Extraterrestrial Intelligence and the Christian Doctrine of Redemption', *Science & Christian Belief,* 1997, 9 (No. 1), pp. 21–34.

Christ. For Christ's sacrifice to be sufficient it is essential that Christ have a human nature. As the *Heidelberg Catechism* (1563) puts it,

God will not punish another creature for the sin which man has committed (*Lord's Day 5*).

He (Christ) must be true man because the justice of God requires that the same human nature which has sinned should pay for sin (*Lord's Day 6*).

The main pertinent biblical reference is found in Hebrews 2:14-17:

Forasmuch then as the children are partakers of flesh and blood, he also himself likewise took part of the same . . . For verily he took not on him the nature of angels; but he took on him the seed of Abraham. Wherefore in all things it behoved him to be made like unto his brethren, that he might be a merciful and faithful high priest in things pertaining to God, to make reconciliation for the sins of the people.

It follows that, since ETs, like the angels, are not descendants of Adam and thus share neither his nature nor his guilt, Christ's sacrifice is of no avail to them. The uniqueness of Christ's incarnation implies the uniqueness also of man as the only creature to be thereby saved from the consequences of his sinfulness. Of course, this does not, by itself, imply that ETs cannot exist, but only rules out their possible redemption through Christ's incarnation.

The notion of unredeemed species is not without precedent. Of the other known species of intelligent beings – angels – we know that there is no redemption for those who fall. Even for fallen man, the redemption is effective only for the elect. Why, then, should it be thought necessary that ETs be redeemed?

As to Davis' reference to Colossians 1:15–20, the Bible makes clear that Christ's reconciliation of all things to himself does not imply that all creatures are to be redeemed. Rather, it concerns Christ's victory over Satan and sin, with the resultant cleansing of creation under the dominion of Christ.

3. The Uniqueness of Man

Even if Davis's argument were valid, it would still imply that man is in a special relation to God, since, from among all possible creatures, Christ chose to take on the specific nature of man. This brings us to a further argument against ETs: the special position of man in the universe. According to Genesis 1, man alone was created in the image of God, and man alone was appointed to have dominion over creation. Even stars were created primarily to serve as lights and signs for man. Finally, at the end of times, Christ returns to the *earth*, the abode of man, to judge living and dead. Man is to judge the angels (*1 Cor.* 6:3). The New Jerusalem comes down from heaven to *earth*. All this reinforces the special place of man in God's creation.

Hence, in the extremely unlikely event that intelligent beings do exist on other planets, we can conclude, on the basis of the biblical account of salvation, that either they have not fallen from grace or, less happily, that, like the angels, there is no redemption for those who fell.

4. Extra-Terrestrial Life

What about primitive extra-terrestrial life? The celestial bodies, created on the fourth day, contain at least some features such as light, water, earthly elements, atmospheric gases, identical to those created in the previous days. Why, then, could they not contain also primitive forms of life, such as vegetation, which were created on the third day? Nevertheless, it must be recalled that the prime purpose of the earth's vegetation is to serve as food for more advanced forms of earthly life, such as man and beast (*Gen.* 1:29–30). No mention is made here of non-earthly vegetation. It would seem that there is no purpose in creating primitive forms of life elsewhere unless this would serve higher forms of life there. Similarly, what would be the function of higher forms of life, such as animals, in the absence of intelligent life, such as man?

The detection of ETL would certainly generate fewer theological questions than would the detection of ETI. On the other hand, the actual detection of ETL is much more difficult. Searches for ETL are essentially limited, at least for the next few decades, to within our own solar system, where the most likely places have already been ruled out.

Conclusions

In conclusion we note that there is no scientific evidence in support of the belief in ETI. On the contrary, there has been no sign of life of any form on any of our planets. All searches for ETI have yielded purely negative results. Searches for interstellar life, scanning nearby stars for radio signals or noise indicative of civilization, have virtually ruled out the possibility of advanced civilized life within a hundred light years. To span greater distances, even an extremely fast rocket travelling at a tenth of the speed of light would take longer than a millennium, and radio dialogues would have century-long gaps. Thus, for all practical purposes, communication with extra-terrestrial civilizations can be ruled out.

From an evolutionary perspective, the odds are so heavily stacked against the chance occurrence of life, particularly intelligent life, that the existence of ETI must be considered extremely improbable.

Creationist arguments for ETI are strongly dependent upon our views regarding the nature of God and his relation to his cosmos. Theological considerations based on biblical revelation weigh very heavily against the presence of ETI, but not conclusively so. In a young universe, it is very improbable that ETI, even if it existed, would be detected in the near future. The case against more primitive forms of extra-terrestrial life is much weaker. Arguing against the existence of ETL are its absence in the biblical creation account and the question as to what purpose the creation of ETL would serve, given the non-existence of ETI. But, again, these considerations do not definitely rule out ETL.

The Future of Life in the Universe

What lies ahead for the universe? Most cosmologists are fairly optimistic regarding the near future – that is, the first few billion years. If man and society have arisen purely through evolution, then it is not unreasonable to posit further evolutionary advances. By modern cosmological standards humans are present in the universe at a very early time in its history and, hence, we must expect our species to be replaced by more advanced forms of life in the future. A few million years down the road intelligent life may be as far removed from us as we presently are from the apes.

According to Frank Tipler, this has important implications for religion:

Traditional religion must come to grips with the fleeting existence of our species in universal history. It is our relative insignificance in time, not space, which is the real challenge posed by modern cosmology for traditional religion.[1]

Tipler emphasizes that the universe will continue to exist for at least 5 billion years:

> Almost all Christian theologians adopt a much shorter temporal perspective. This is as great an error – and as great a misunderstanding of mankind's place in nature – as believing that the universe was created a few thousand years ago.[2]

Presumably Tipler believes that Christianity will no longer be applicable to the advanced species of the future. To this it must be pointed out that improved intelligence and technology would do little to eradicate man's main deficiency: a sinful heart. The need for a Saviour would still remain. However, Tipler does make the valid point that the future as depicted by the big-bang universe is as much at odds with that of traditional Christianity as is its description of origins.

While the relatively near future may seem rather secure for civilization, in the long run the picture is far from rosy. A number of factors point to a gloomy fate, not only for civilization but also for life itself. According to the big-bang theory, if the density of the universe is greater than a critical amount, then the universe is finite, its expansion will gradually slow down, contraction will set in and it will end in a Big Crunch. The universe may still bounce back, but all life would have been destroyed.

On the other hand, if the cosmic density is less than the critical amount – and this seems to be the case – then the universe is predicted to continue to expand forever. As available energy is irretrievably lost and the temperature drops, the universe approaches its inevitable heat death (actually a 'cold death'). Again it would seem that life eventually disappears.

With such gloomy prospects regarding the fate of life in the universe, it is not surprising that Steven Weinberg concludes his popular book *The First Three Minutes* with these words:

> The more the universe seems comprehensible, the more it also appears pointless. But if there is no solace in the fruits of the research, there is

---

[1] 'The Omega Point Theory: A Model of an Evolving God', *in* Russell (ed.), *Physics, Philosophy and Theology*, 1988, p. 313.   [2] *Ibid.,* p. 316.

at least some consolation in the research itself . . . The effort to understand the universe is one of the very few things that lifts human life a little above the level of farce, and gives it some of the grace of tragedy.[1]

Most cosmologists share such a pessimistic outlook for the possibility of the long-term survival of life. However, such a gloomy forecast has been challenged by a few optimists who envision at least a possibility that life may emerge victorious. Let us examine a few of these alternatives.

Future Life in a Closed Universe

Among big-bang cosmologists, Frank Tipler and Freeman Dyson are two exceptions who paint a rosier picture for life in the distant future. They differ, however, in their assessment as to whether a closed or an open universe will be more hospitable for life. Whereas Dyson favours an open universe, Tipler believes that only a closed universe will do.[2]

Tipler defines life in terms of information processing. A *living being* is any entity that codes information, with the information coded being preserved through natural selection. With this definition even cars and computers can be considered as forms of life. Tipler asserts that man is a purely physical object that can be regarded as a type of computer. The human mind – or soul – is just a specific computer program run on a computer called the brain. Man has arrived rather early in the evolution of the universe; it must be expected that he will eventually be replaced by more advanced forms of life. The next stage of intelligent life might well be, quite literally, information processing machines.

According to Tipler, the laws of thermodynamics permit an infinite amount of information processing in the future, provided there is sufficient available energy at all future times. The available energy depends on the temperature. Since, in an open universe the temperature eventually becomes too low to support life, Tipler turns to a closed universe. In a closed universe the present expansion will eventually turn into a contraction, at which point the temperature will again increase, approaching infinity as the singularity draws near. As

---

[1] *The First Three Minutes*, New York: Bantam Books, 1979, p. 144.
[2] *The Physics of Immortality*, New York: Doubleday, 1994.

the Big Crunch is approached, life will engulf the entire universe, will be unified into an immense computer that will store an infinite amount of information, and will eventually control all matter and energy sources. This event, which Tipler calls the 'Omega Point', is the culmination of life. Since the Omega Point is omniscient, omnipresent, and omnipotent, Tipler equates it with God.

The Big Crunch, which will be reached in a finite time, will spell an end for life. How, then, does Tipler rescue the immortality of life? According to Tipler the metabolism of life speeds up with the temperature increase, so that an infinite amount of *subjective* time – time as experienced by living beings – will elapse before the singularity is reached.

Although Tipler argues that the Omega Point necessarily exists, few cosmologists agree with him. Indeed, his scenario sounds more like far-out science fiction than factual science. A detailed critique of Tipler's ideas has been made by Ellis and Coule.[1] Among other things, they find Tipler's definition of life to be absurdly simplistic, as contrasted with the incredible complexity of biological life, particularly its intricate control mechanisms determining cellular and bodily functions. They conclude that there are no physically plausible mechanisms that would allow life to occur under the extreme conditions Tipler envisions. Any possible physically based computing machine, let alone living systems, would be destroyed well before the final crunch.

In any event, Tipler makes six testable predictions, of which at least two are currently falsified. Tipler predicts that the universe is closed and that Hubble's constant – the present rate of expansion – is at most 45 km/sec/mpc (mpc stands for 'megaparsec', a distance of about 3 million light years). Current observations, at least as interpreted by big-bang astronomers, indicate that the universe is open and that Hubble's constant is about 70 km/sec/mpc.

Future Life in an Open Universe

Let us now consider the possibility of life in an open universe. Dyson, contrary to Tipler, sees no future for life if the universe is finite and closed. In that case the universe will eventually contract, the sky will

---

[1] G. F. R. Ellis and D. H. Coule, 'Life at the End of the Universe', *General Relativity and Gravitation,* 1994, 26, pp. 713–39.

grow hotter and hotter until it finally falls in on us as we approach a space-time singularity at infinite temperature. No life could survive such a fate. Life would barely be able to spread itself around the cosmos before it meets its demise.[1]

On the other hand, if the universe is open and infinite, then Dyson finds more hope. In that case the universe will expand forever, growing colder as it does. Life now faces the prospect of slow freezing rather than quick frying. However, Dyson believes that it is easier for life to adapt to cold than to heat.

Dyson, like Tipler, assumes that the essence of life resides in *organization* rather than in *substance*. The basis of life lies in *structure*, in the way molecules are organized, rather than in the substance of the molecules themselves. If this assumption is true, then one can imagine life detached from flesh and blood and embodied in such complex entities as networks of superconducting circuitry or even in interstellar dust clouds.

The complexity of life can be measured in terms of bits of information. For information processing the main consideration is not an abundant energy supply, but rather a good signal-to-noise ratio. The colder the environment, the quieter the background noise, and thus the more thrifty life can be in its use of energy. As the universe gets colder the pulse of life will slow down but will never stop. As in Tipler's scheme, man is destined to become extinct but the torch of life will continually be passed on to ever more hardy forms of life.

One prediction of particle physics is that all matter may be unstable. Theory predicts that after 10^{33} years the nuclei of all atoms will have decayed into positrons, photons, and neutrons. This may pose a severe test for life, but Dyson is confident that life will again adapt to the new circumstances. According to Dyson, the total energy reserve contained in the sun would be sufficient to support forever a society with a complexity 10 trillion times greater than our own. This energy would also suffice to keep open forever as many communication channels as would be needed to keep us talking with every star in the visible part of the universe.

No matter how far into the future we go, there will always be new things happening: new information coming in and new worlds to

[1] F. Dyson, *Infinite in All Directions*, New York: Harper & Row, 1988, pp. 107–15.

explore. Life and intelligence are potentially immortal, with resources of knowledge and memory constantly growing as the temperature of the universe decreases and the reserves of free energy dwindle. Nevertheless, as Dyson himself is the first to admit, this sketch of the future is highly speculative, based more on a highly fertile and optimistic imagination than on hard scientific knowledge.

Future Life in a Plasma Cosmology

A further possibility for future life has been presented by Eric Lerner, who rejects big-bang cosmology.[1] Lerner promotes a plasma cosmology that postulates the universe to be infinite in both space and time. According to him, the pessimistic conclusions of conventional cosmology are false. Thermodynamics does not demand that the universe will wind down. Lerner assures us that we need not worry about a heat death, for there can be ever-increasing orders of complexity, with increasing energy flows. The heat death can be indefinitely postponed as technology devises ever more efficient machines. This would preclude both an end to life and an end to the growth of life.

Lerner believes that there is a strong correlation between society and cosmology. The current pessimistic, finite-big-bang model is mirrored by a pessimistic spirit in today's society. According to Lerner, 'When society retreats, when progress is halted, rationality is discredited and many turn to the supernatural.' He argues that the universe is not doomed, that we need not despair, that our present actions can permanently change the cosmos and will be echoed through a limitless future, even though there is no hope for individual immortality. One major drawback with this model is its denial, not only of big-bang cosmology, but, more fundamentally, also of the validity of the second law of thermodynamics as applied to the universe as a whole. Another is its postulation of a hypothetical ever-increasing complexity. Here, too, we have a very speculative sketch of the future that has attracted few supporters.

Conclusions

In summary, although a few optimistic scenarios of a rosy future have been concocted, it appears extremely unlikely that, in a naturalistic

[1] *The Big Bang Never Happened*, New York: Times Books, 1991.

universe, life can survive indefinitely long. Modern cosmology offers little hope for the distant future, either for individuals, or for the human race, or even for the survival of life as such.

In recent times a number of Christians have tried to establish a harmony between modern cosmology and Christianity. Rather than having the two conflict or be totally independent, they have treated them as separate disciplines leading to the same truths but asking different questions. The big-bang model of origins is often acclaimed as God's way of creating. Genesis is then limited to telling us who did it; modern cosmology tells us the how and when. It has been argued that origins is not of crucial importance, that the basics of Christianity could still be salvaged within big-bang cosmology. If the big bang is to be seen as God's way of creating, must we likewise consider the Big Crunch (or the Big Whimper) as God's way of ending the universe? Must Revelation share the same hermeneutical fate as Genesis? That, at least, would be consistent. Yet it is obvious that this would leave little substance to Christianity. The central message of Christianity includes the return of Christ, the Last Judgment, and life everlasting in a new heaven and a new earth. And this is coming soon, not billions of years in the future. The biblical conception of the future differs greatly from that of modern cosmology.

Such considerations have led physicist-turned-theologian John Polkinghorne, a firm adherent to the big-bang account of the origin of the universe, to reject big-bang eschatology. He believes that Christians can hope for a personal, as well as a cosmic resurrection, but that faith must be grounded upon God and his mercy rather than on physics. Thus, at the end, Polkinghorne does place his faith in the supernatural beyond the physical. The death of life in the universe can be avoided, it seems, only through miraculous means.[1]

The same conclusion is reached by Ted Peters, another big-bang proponent, who writes:

> Eschatological hope for redemption is drawn from the interpretation of biblical symbols. It comes strictly from theological resources, not scientific evidence. The prospects of heat death due to the law of entropy might even be interpreted as a possible disconfirmation of theological

---

[1] *The Faith of a Physicist*, Princeton: The University Press, 1994.

affirmation. We will have to admit that at the present stage of inquiry there exists very little consonance between theology and physics regarding the ultimate future of the cosmos.[2]

Conversely, the lack of consonance could be interpreted as a disconfirmation of big-bang cosmology. Insistence upon biblical eschatology implies that, at some point, Christians must part company with big-bang cosmology. But if Christianity must reject big-bang extrapolations into the distant future, why should it accept big-bang extrapolations into the past? At the very least, these eschatological considerations should stimulate Christians to re-evaluate big-bang cosmology and their commitment to it.

[2] 'The Trinity in and beyond Time', *in* J. R. Russell, N. Murphy and C. J. Isham (eds.), *Quantum Cosmology and the Laws of Nature: Scientific Perspectives on Divine Action,* Vatican City: Vatican Observatory Publications, 1996.

6

The Strange Gods of
Modern Cosmology

Two chief concerns of religion are the nature of God and what this implies for our life after death. In a previous chapter we discussed the implications drawn from modern cosmology concerning the existence of God. There we noted that, at best, the evidence can suggest only a Prime Mover or Designer, a deistic being that falls far short of the living God of the Bible. We shall now examine a selection of gods that have been constructed to fit into various cosmological models. To what extent can these be reconciled with traditional Christianity? In particular, we shall be concerned with comparing the modern gods with the biblical God and investigating what kind of hope they offer regarding individual immortality.

The Evolving God of Natural Theology

Basic to modern cosmology is the notion of evolution: that the entire universe and its contents has developed from the initial singularity. If God is a natural being, a being placed entirely within the confines of the physical universe, then it follows that God, too, must be evolving. Thus the God of modern cosmology is generally conceived, if at all, as an evolving God.

The notion of an evolving God can be traced back to the German idealist philosopher Friedrich Schelling (1775–1854), who, in 1810, was the first to introduce a radical evolutionism into metaphysics and theology. According to Schelling, God is subject to suffering and change, and will become perfect only in the distant future, at the final state of the universe. God is identified with the evolutionary process, or, at least, with the not-yet-realized final result of the process.

These revolutionary ideas were taken up and reworked by the French philosopher Henri Bergson (1859–1941) in his book *Creative Evolution*, published in 1907. He believed that, metaphysically, *becoming* was more basic than *being*. Evolution was considered to be a creative force in the sense that it always engendered something wholly new, something unexpected. Nature was viewed as an organic whole, ultimately purposeful because it is driven by a non-physical, impersonal Life Force, whose future and goals are ultimately unknowable.[1] Although Bergson was aware of the inevitable thermo-dynamic Heat Death, he suggested that life may be able to take a form in which the Heat Death was delayed indefinitely. Bergson was to have a great influence on another Frenchman, the Jesuit Teilhard de Chardin, to be discussed presently.

A decade later another version of an evolving God was developed, this time in England by Samuel Alexander (1859–1938). Alexander's fundamental entity was Space-Time. This generates first matter, then life, and finally mind. Beyond mind there is yet a further, much superior, stage, which Alexander termed 'deity'. As mind can exist in a living being, so deity can exist in mind; but most minds will not possess deity, in the same manner as most living beings do not possess mind. The purpose of the universe is to bring deity into being. Beings with finite deity are finite gods. God includes the whole universe, although his deity is lodged in only a portion of it. According to Alexander, such an evolving God has not always existed, but will come into existence at some future time.

Natural Evolving Gods

In more recent times the notion of an evolving god has been advanced by several authors. First, we shall examine a number of proposals from scientists who have no sympathy with Christianity. Their gods

---

[1] See the analysis by Barrow and Tipler, *The Anthropic Cosmological Principle*, p. 90. Throughout this section I am much indebted to their treatment.

are erected presumably from purely non-revelationary considerations. Hence we could call these the gods of natural theology. These
gods are purely natural, purportedly involving only natural causes
and effects. Later we shall investigate various proposals by theologians as to how to incorporate some form of Christian God into an
evolving cosmos.

1. The God of Paul Davies

First we consider the natural god proposed by physicist Paul Davies
in his book, *God and the New Physics*. Davies writes, 'It may seem
bizarre, but in my opinion science offers a surer path to God than
religion.' He is convinced that the scientific evidence favours the
existence of a God. What has convinced Davies that God must exist?
He cites a number of factors:

> It is clear that no order at all could exist unless the universe as a whole
> started out with a considerable stock of negative entropy. If total disor-
> der always increases, in accordance with the second law, then the
> universe must, it seems, have been created in an orderly condition. Does
> this not provide strong evidence in favour of a creator-designer? . . . If
> the universe is simply an accident, the odds against it containing an
> appreciable order are ludicrously small.[1]

He finds that there are many mysteries about the natural world that
would readily be explained by postulating a natural God. Davies is
quite impressed by the apparent fine-tuning of the universe. He
writes:

> It is hard to resist the impression that the present structure of the uni-
> verse, apparently so sensitive to minor alterations in the numbers [of the
> fundamental physical constants], has been rather carefully thought
> out.[2]

He notes in particular the puzzle of the origin of galaxies and of
life. Nevertheless, Davies is careful to avoid the 'god of the gaps' trap.
He argues that 'To invoke God as a blanket explanation of the unexplained is to invite eventual falsification, and to make God the friend
of ignorance.'[3]

---

[1] *God and the New Physics,* pp. 166–7.
[2] *Ibid.*, p. 189.   [3] *Ibid.*, p. 209

Although Davies is convinced that there must be a God, he objects to a supernatural God. He insists that miracles, being repugnant to scientists, are to be avoided. A natural God, Davies believes, is more plausible than a supernatural one:

> The hypothesis that a natural God created life, within the laws of physics, is at least known to be possible and consistent with our scientific understanding of the physical world.[1]

Davies suggests that:

> It is possible to imagine a supermind existing since the creation, encompassing all the fundamental fields of nature, and taking upon itself the task of converting an incoherent big bang into the complex and orderly we now observe; all accomplished entirely within the framework of the laws of physics. This would not be a God who created everything by supernatural means, but a directing, controlling, universal mind pervading the cosmos and operating the laws of nature to achieve some specific purpose . . . Nature is a product of its own technology, and that universe is a mind: a self-observing as well as self-organizing system.[2]

He suggests such a mind can 'load the quantum dice', thereby controlling everything that happens, and can thus escape our attention. This God would be the creator of everything we see, having made matter from pre-existing energy and set up the necessary conditions for life, but he would not be capable of creation out of nothing, as Christian doctrine requires. Davies is of the opinion that 'such a picture of God might well be enough to satisfy most believers'.

A number of questions come to mind. For one, how can a purely natural being 'load the quantum dice', as Davies puts it? To invoke such a concept, going beyond known physics, smacks of the 'god of the gaps' thinking that Davies expressly wishes to avoid. A further major deficiency is that Davies fails to explain how such a natural God could arise in the first place. To explain the apparent order in the universe Davies invokes a Designer. But if this designer itself is the result of purely natural forces, as Davies contends, its origin is even more in need of explanation. Davies attempts to explain one mystery by appealing to an immensely greater one. Since he limits himself to purely natural explanations, his solution seems highly implausible. Only a supernatural creator can do the job Davies requires of him.

---

[1] *Ibid.*, p. 209.   [2] *Ibid.*, p. 210.

Further, the power of Davies' God is very limited. Controlling only quantum states, it is still bound by the laws of physics. It can do no miracles. Consequently, it offers man no hope for a life hereafter. Indeed, the divine mind itself, being purely natural, cannot hope to escape eventual destruction, whether via the heat death or the Big Crunch.

In short, this is not a God that demands worship or answers prayer. Hence, contrary to Davies' optimistic expectations, this 'God' is unlikely to satisfy many religious needs.

2. *The God of Freeman Dyson*

Another attempt to create a natural god has been made by physicist Freeman Dyson in his book *Infinite in All Directions*. We have already considered Dyson's optimistic view of the future. As the reader may recall, Dyson argues for the eternal survival of life in the universe.

To Dyson the most astounding fact of the universe is the power of mind that drives our bodies. Mind, through biological evolution, has established itself as a driving force in our little corner of the universe. The tendency of mind to infiltrate and control matter is a fundamental law of nature. Dyson writes:

> Mind is patient. Mind has waited for 3 billion years on this planet before composing its first string quartet. It may have to wait for another 3 billion years before it spreads all over the galaxy.[1]

When mind has further expanded its organization by many orders of magnitude beyond the human scale then we can no more expect to understand its thoughts than a butterfly can understand ours. At that stage it may be called 'God'.

Dyson considers God to be either a world-soul or a collection of world-souls. At the present stage of development we may be considered to be the chief inlets of God on this planet. Dyson's God is neither omniscient nor omnipotent, but one who learns and grows as the universe unfolds. As such, the universe is not deterministic but open. Chance is part of God's plan; chance exists because God shares our ignorance. Dyson considers this God to be close to the one of process theology, which will be discussed later.

[1] *Infinite in All Directions*, p. 118.

The universe, according to Dyson, has a deep purpose. He asserts:

I believe that we are here to some purpose, that the purpose has something to do with the future, and that it transcends altogether the limits of our knowledge and understanding . . . If you like, you can call the transcendent purpose God. If it is God, it is a Socinian God, inherent in the universe and growing in power and knowledge as the universe unfolds. Our minds are not only expressions of its purpose but are also contributions to its growth.[1]

The word *Socinian*, used by Dyson, refers to the radical Italian theologian Lelio Sozzini (Socinus) (1525–62), who denied original sin, the deity of Christ, the Trinity, and predestination.

Regarding scientific evidence for God, Dyson writes:

The argument from design is a theological and not a scientific argument . . . I consider the argument from design to be valid in the following sense. The universe shows evidence of the operation of mind on three levels. The first level is the level of elementary physical processes in quantum mechanics. Matter in quantum mechanics is not an inert substance but an active agent, constantly making choices between alternative possibilities according to probabilistic laws . . . It appears that mind, as manifested by the capacity to make choices, is to some extent inherent in every electron. The second level at which we detect the operation of mind is the level of direct human experience. Our brains appear to be devices for the amplification of the mental component of the quantum choices made by the molecules inside our head. We are the second big step in the development of mind. Now comes the argument from design. There is evidence from peculiar features of the laws of nature that the universe as a whole is hospitable to the growth of mind . . . Therefore it is reasonable to believe in the existence of a third level of mind, a mental component of the universe. If we believe in this mental component and call it God, then we can say that we are small pieces of God's mental apparatus.[2]

To know the ultimate purpose of the universe we must read God's mind. Dyson suggests the universe is constructed according to a principle of maximum diversity, both at the physical and mental levels. The laws of nature and initial conditions are such as to make the

---

[1] *Ibid.*, p. 294.   [2] *Ibid.*, p. 297.

universe as interesting as possible. As a result, life is possible but not too easy.

Dyson's description of a natural god is more developed than that of Davies, yet there are many similarities. Both envision God as an evolved supermind. Both point to the argument from design as evidence for the existence of such a god. Yet neither offers an explanation as to how this supermind, who really comes into his own in the far future, could have influenced the initial conditions and subsequent evolution up to now. Design is explained in terms of a designer who, in turn, is supposed to be the product of a purely natural process. This merely adds to the complexity of the design problem without making any progress in explaining it.

Self-Caused Gods

The main difficulty with a natural god is accounting for its origin. A number of proposals have been made to remedy this deficiency.

1. The God of Fred Hoyle

Fred Hoyle, in his book *The Intelligent Universe*, describes his perplexity with the emergence of life on earth. On the basis of the intricate complexity of life, he finds the transformation of non-life to life to be so improbable that he doubts it has occurred on earth. Instead, Hoyle postulates that life, in the form of bacteria, came to the earth from outer space.

In particular, Hoyle puzzles over the fact that life, and other features in cosmology, appears to operate contrary to the second law of thermodynamics. Instead of disintegrating and collapsing, like other physical systems, living matter becomes more and more organized. To explain this unusual behaviour, he resorts to a rather bizarre idea: that evolution is guided by information *from the future!* Hoyle believes that biological systems are somehow working backwards in time:

> On a cosmic scale the effect of introducing information from the future would be . . . far-reaching. Instead of the Universe beginning in the wound-up state of the big bang, degenerating ever since, an initially primitive state of affairs could wind itself up gradually as time proceeds, becoming more, not less sophisticated, from past to future. This would allow the accumulation of information – information without

which the evolution of life, and of the Universe itself, makes no logical sense.[1]

Furthermore, Hoyle believes that Darwin's theory is wrong: random variations lead nowhere. For progress to occur genetic information must come from outside the system. Furthermore:

> We have seen that life could not have originated here on the earth. Nor does it look as though biological evolution can be explained from within an earth-bound theory of life. Genes from outside the earth are needed to drive the evolutionary process ... A proper understanding of evolution requires that the environment, or the variations on which it operates, or both, be intelligently controlled.[2]

What is the source of this mysterious source of this information from the future, which controls the evolutionary process? According to Hoyle it is an intelligence, placed infinitely far in the future. Such an intelligence explains the various anthropic coincidences noted in a previous chapter. It also explains the occurrence of geniuses such as Mozart and Shakespeare.

Hoyle stresses that this being is not an omnipotent, supernatural God:

> The intelligence responsible for the creation of carbon-based life in the cosmic theory is firmly within the universe and is subservient to it. Because the creator of carbon-based life was not all-powerful, there is consequently no paradox in the fact that terrestrial life is far from ideal.[3]

Hoyle does not claim to know where this god is to be located, what it does, or what its physical form is. This god acquires full stature only in the distant future. To influence the past and present, Hoyle resorts to the novel conception of backward causation. The intelligence works in a reversed-time sense, from future to past, by controlling individual quantum events. Only thus can it bring about its own existence:

> The overriding intelligence of the infinite future, which masterminds the development of intelligence in our present time, must exercise its controlling influence simply in order to exist.[4]

---

[1] *The Intelligent Universe*, p. 214.   [2] *Ibid.*, p. 242, 244.   [3] *Ibid.*, p. 236.
[4] *Ibid.*, p. 248.

Hoyle claims that it is illogical for God to influence the universe and yet not be affected by it, as he claims is the case for the Christian God. This, he asserts, is avoided by his 'God', who exists only by virtue of the support received from the universe. Hoyle complains that the idea of a 'normal cause and effect' intelligence, such as he advocates, is not well received in the contemporary western world because, in conformity with Christian tradition, it is the wish of western astronomers to invoke supernatural ultimate causes from outside the universe.

It should be noted that Hoyle, in this book, rejects both the big-bang and steady-state theories. Instead, he opts for an eternal universe of many little bangs. Thus he is not faced with the problem of the creation of the entire universe in time.

What are we to make of this? To explain the apparent design in the universe Hoyle points to a Designer. But if this intelligence is to be natural then it must have evolved, and could not have been there in any effective form near the beginning. Yet the major anthropic coincidences that must be explained, such as the expansion rate and the value of the physical constants, must presumably be set at a very early stage in the development of the cosmos. Hence, if there is a Designer, He must have been designing from the beginning, implying a supernatural being who existed before the creation of the cosmos.

Scoffing at those who wish to invoke such a supernatural cause, Hoyle resorts to the doubtful alternative of backward causation. But this is hardly 'normal cause and effect'; this is no less than miraculous. Hoyle's God is really one with supernatural powers, albeit of a limited kind. Again, there is no hope for an after-life, and nothing in Hoyle's God that instils fear or love in us.

2. The God of Frank Tipler

A much more ambitious model for an evolving god has been developed by Frank Tipler,[1] in most detail in his book *The Physics of Immortality*. According to Tipler, the war between science and Christianity is over. Science has found God and theology has been

---

[1] 'The Omega Point Theory: A Model of an Evolving God', *in* Russell, *Physics, Philosophy and Theology,* 1988; 'The Omega Point as Eschaton: Answers to Pannenberg's Questions for Scientists', *Zygon,* 1989, 24, pp. 217–53; *The Physics of Immortality*, New York: Doubleday, 1994.

reduced to a mere branch of physical cosmology. Tipler presents his Omega Point Theory as

> a testable physical theory for an omniscient, omnipotent God who will one day resurrect every single one of us to live forever in an abode which is in all essentials the Judeo-Christian heaven.[1]

The reader may recall, from our discussion of Tipler in the previous chapter, that he assumes a closed universe, where the present expansion will eventually turn into a contraction, leading ultimately to the Big Crunch. Life is defined essentially as information processing. As the Big Crunch is approached, life will engulf the entire universe. It will become omnipresent, omnipotent, and omniscient in the sense that it will control all matter and energy sources, while storing an infinite amount of information. Tipler calls this event – the final singularity – the 'Omega Point'. Since the Omega Point is just beyond space-time it is 'transcendent'; since it is formally equivalent to all space-time points it is also 'immanent' in every point in space-time. Tipler believes that, due to its high intelligence, the Omega Point counts as a person. The Omega Point will 'experience' the whole of universal history 'all at once', as in the theological notion of eternity. In Tipler's model, God and the universe are two aspects of the same thing, but his theory is not quite a form of pantheism.

Although Tipler calls this god 'omnipotent', because it controls all energy and matter, it must be kept in mind that it is still limited to natural law; and although this god is 'omniscient', its knowledge will not be complete until the Omega Point is reached.

How can we be certain that the Omega Point actually will be reached? The postulate by which Tipler deduces an evolving God is fundamentally a moral one. Value is something connected to life. If value is to remain in the universe, life must persist indefinitely. The laws of physics must therefore permit the existence of life for ever. The continued existence of life implies progressive evolution without limit in space-time: the limit of cosmological and biological evolution is a point beyond space and time, the Omega Point. This brings the concept of purpose back into science: 'Teleology, although removed from terrestrial biology, reappears when biology is combined with cosmology'.[2]

[1] *The Physics of Immortality*, p. 1.   [2] 'The Omega Point Theory', p. 315.

To ensure that we do arrive at the Omega Point, Tipler proposes the 'Teilhard Boundary Condition' for the universal wave function. The universal wave function, which Tipler equates with the Holy Spirit, is the set of all possible histories of the universe. Tipler's condition specifies that all possible histories of the universe end in a future Omega Point, with life coming into existence along at least one history and continuing on to the Omega Point. He conjectures that this boundary condition gives a unique universal wave function.

In that case the laws of physics and every physical thing that exists would in effect be generated by the Omega Point and its living properties. These properties determine the wave function and the wave function determines everything else. The ultimate future guides all present states into itself. In a sense, the Omega Point creates the physical universe, but in another sense the Omega Point creates itself. Tipler's universe is thus completely deterministic: nothing unexpected can happen, everything is fixed by the universal wave function.

It should be noted that Tipler explicitly states that he is not a Christian but, rather, an atheist – at least until his theory is confirmed, at which point he will become a theist. He regards his model, allegedly based on natural processes alone, as a challenge to the existence of the traditional Christian God.

Again, a major flaw is that some form of backward causation is necessary in order to have this god create itself. Everything is predetermined by the wave function, but how is this wave function established in the first place?

As noted in the previous chapter, present observations rule out a closed universe, which is required in Tipler's model. Further, as pointed out by cosmologist George Ellis in a devastating review,[1] Tipler ignores the fact that the indefinitely rising temperature would dissociate matter into its fundamental constituents, making reliable storage and processing of information impossible. Ellis comments:

> One cannot point out in a short review all the absurdities in this extraordinary edifice, which is the product of a fertile and creative imagination unhampered by the normal constraints of scientific or philosophical discipline. Tipler does not merely base his theory on highly improbable assumptions and make claims that cannot by any

---

[1] 'Piety in the Sky', *Nature*, 1994, *371*, p. 115.

stretch of the imagination be tested by experiment or observation; he typically assigns the label 'God' to a mathematical construction that, while it might possibly be a good description of the causal boundary of the universe (it probably is not), certainly does not refer in any serious sense to what the word 'God' is normally taken to refer to.

In summary, these natural gods are not likely to attract many believers. Subject as they are to natural law (except for backward causation!), they can perform no miracles, answer no prayers, and have few of the characteristics generally attributed to the God of the Bible. Moreover, since they could not have existed prior to the (presumed) big-bang singularity and will not evolve into superminds for a long time, their past and present influence can be brought about only through such dubious ploys as backward causation, which seems to boil down merely to a special form of supernaturalism, albeit in disguise.

An Evolving God and Christianity

A number of attempts have been made to construct evolving gods that are more in accord with Christianity. We shall examine the views of Teilhard de Chardin and of process theology, both of which have been fairly influential.

1. The God of Teilhard de Chardin

Pierre Teilhard de Chardin (1881–1955) was a Jesuit priest as well as a paleontologist (that is, a fossil expert). He was much concerned with adapting Christianity to the modern world view, attempting to demonstrate that Christianity is the religion of evolution. The Roman Catholic Church forbade the publication of his radical views on evolutionary Christianity during his lifetime and they became widely known only after his death. His main work was *The Phenomenon of Man*.[1] Teilhard's views have not been without influence. For example, Frank Tipler identifies a number of facets in his model that are very similar to those of Teilhard's model. Hence his reference to the 'Teilhard' boundary condition and to Teilhard's 'Omega Point'.

Pondering over the mysterious relationship between matter and consciousness, two seemingly quite different entities, Teilhard rejected the usual notion that consciousness somehow developed

---

[1] London: Collins, 1959.

from matter. Instead, Teilhard started from the hypothesis of the primacy of psychism. He considered self-consciousness to be the fundamental entity in the universe, being already present in matter from the beginning. All material things, living or not, have a psychic side, a 'within', and a material side, a 'without'.[1] The evolutionary process was viewed as having a dual nature: a growing outward complexity as well as a growing inward psychism, both culminating in man. The future course of evolution is contained in man. The unity being attained throughout the various arts and sciences is indicative of the convergence of evolution in and through man.

Ultimately, when the highest possible unification and consciousness have been attained, a central point is reached, called the Omega Point. This Omega Point, the goal of creation, is identified as Christ. Christ is thus seen as the unifying principle of the cosmos, since everything is ultimately held together in him, the energizing principle in the cosmos, since all motion originates from the final object, and also the principle of completion, since everything finds its ultimate perfection in him.

But this Christocentric future is by no means certain! The completion of the world in Christ can be accomplished only through the co-operation of man. Since man is free, it is within his power to make the project fail.[2] Thus, as Wildiers summarizes it,[3] our main concern ought to be the further evolution of man towards greater spiritual unification. There is a mystical element in Teilhard, wherein he identifies the world with God, sometimes referring to his view as a 'Christian pantheism'. He wished to stress the presence of God in all things, particularly in the evolutionary process. God has become immersed in his creation, struggling with it for its completion; God's incarnation is coextensive with the duration of the world. Thus love of the world and love of God are combined into one. Through study and work, social and political action, we unite ourselves with Christ.[4] In short, Teilhard's universe is one where God, who manifests himself in the physical universe in the person of Christ, evolves.

From a scientific perspective, Teilhard believed that his theory faced some thermodynamic difficulties. The evolution of ever-more-complex entities seemed to him to be contrary to the Second Law of

---

[1] *The Phenomenon of Man*, p. 59.   [2] *Ibid.*, p. 307.
[3] *The Theologian and His Universe*, p. 207.   [4] *Ibid.*, p. 210.

thermodynamics, with its prediction of a general trend toward disorder, rather than order. Also, the Heat Death predicted by this law would rule out the future eternal existence of the Christic Omega Point. Eventually even Christ would die a permanent death.

To overcome these limitations Teilhard argued for the existence of another form of energy – a 'radial' or psychic energy – in addition to the usual physical 'tangential' energy. Since all forms of matter contain some psychic substance, psychic radial energy is available in all matter. It provides a vital force that drives the evolutionary process. Its concentration increases as evolution progresses upwards towards greater complexity.

In man, radial energy is the energy in our thoughts. Radial and tangential energy are somehow related and pass into each other. On the one hand, 'to think, we must eat',[1] on the other hand, through thought and will we can effect physical change.

According to Teilhard radial energy would oppose the degenerative effects of the second law. Since Teilhard wrote this, it has been noted that his psychic, radial energy is in fact equivalent to information content, which cannot avoid the restrictions of the second law.[2] Thus, as a scientific theory, this aspect of Teilhard's view has been refuted.

Although Teilhard's universe does centre about Christ, it is a much diminished Christ who is heavily dependent upon man's efforts and the evolutionary process. Hardly the Christ of orthodox Christianity.

2. The God of Process Theology

In recent years process thought has become increasingly popular among theologians. This movement originated with the work of Alfred North Whitehead (1861-1947) who, in his earlier years, had been active in the philosophy of science and mathematics. He was much influenced by the writings of Bergson and Alexander. In his main work, *Process and Reality*,[3] he developed a metaphysical system in which the central notions were those of *process* and *becoming*. His ideas have since been further developed by a number of theologians and philosophers, the foremost among his followers being Charles Hartshorne and Schubert Ogden.

---

[1] *The Phenomenon of Man*, p. 64.
[2] Barrow and Tipler, *The Anthropic Cosmological Principle*, p. 198.
[3] New York: Macmillan, 1929.

Process theology rejects both the God of classical theism, where God is distinct from the world, and pantheism, which equates God with the world. Instead, it adopts a view called 'panentheism', which means 'all in God'. The world is seen as the body of God. God also has a mind, but this is dependent upon his body. Creatures in the universe are considered cells of God's body.

Whitehead considers God to be 'dipolar': he has both a *primordial* nature and a *consequent* nature. Viewed as primordial, God is 'the unlimited conceptual realization of the absolute wealth of potentiality'.[1] In this state he has no consciousness. Through this aspect God is the source of unity and order in the world. 'He is the lure for feeling, the eternal urge of desire'.[2] In this pole God is infinite and unchanging.

But there is also another side to God. In his consequent nature God is conscious, and is 'the realization of the actual world in the unity of his nature, and through the transformation of his wisdom'.[3] In this pole God is finite, dependent upon the world, and in process. 'God is the great companion – the fellow sufferer who understands.'[4] God is both the primordial ground of order, structuring potential forms of relationships before they are actualized, and the ground of novelty, presenting new possibilities.

Not only God – at least in his primordial nature – but also the universe is eternal. God created the world, not *ex nihilo*, but out of pre-existing material. God is not *before* all creation but *with* all creation. Nor is our universe the only universe. Over time, all logically possible universes ('cosmic epochs') will come into existence, each ultimately to be replaced by its successor; ours, too, will eventually be extinguished.[5]

In process theology God is generally thought to be omniscient with respect to all past and present events, but not with regard to the future. The future is indeterminate and not even God can know it.[6] If the future were fixed there would be no room for free actions by man. Process theology affirms both order and openness in nature. Divine purpose is understood to have unchanging goals but not a detailed eternal plan; God responds to the unpredictable. Process

[1] *Process and Reality,* p. 521.   [2] *Ibid.*, p. 522.   [3] *Ibid.*, p. 524.
[4] *Ibid.*, p. 532.   [5] *Ibid.*, p. 139, 148, 171.
[6] R. H. Nash, *The Concept of God*, Grand Rapids: Academe Books, p. 27.

thought recognizes alternative potentialities that may or may not be realized. The God of process theology is not omnipotent. He influences the world, by valuing particular potentialities to which creatures can respond, but without determining events. God always acts with and through other entities, rather than acting alone as a substitute for their actions. God's presence in the universe is thus not readily detectable. Most process theologians believe that God's acting does not contradict science and, hence, that God does not perform miracles. God's power over nature is limited. The power God exercises is that of evoking love and inspiration, rather than controlling, unilateral power. God does not compel, but provides creative power to his creatures.

It is through man that God has the greatest opportunities to influence the world. Man is considered as a free being, co-creator with God and of God. Man creates himself through the decisions he makes. Also on the material and biological levels 'decisions' are made when one of many possibilities is realized. The world is a series of decisions and in this sense freedom forms a dimension of the universe. Not only man, but the whole world is a self-creative reality. All events that take place are mutually related. The fundamental properties of reality are creativity and relativity, with God being the supreme Creativity and the universal Relation.

The cohesion of all the individual decisions in the world is due to the influence of a supreme creativity on all events. This does not cancel their freedom but is a form of enticement. God is that ordering element whereby creativity assumes a specific character and without which no occasions of experience are possible. God is the ever-present ground of experience. Every occasion is dependent on God for its existence as well as for the order of possibilities it can actualize. Unlike Teilhard's view of the culmination of history in an Omega Point, process theology envisions history as having no specific ultimate goal. There is only a deity growing ever more towards increasing perfection.

Ronald Nash has criticized process theology on a number of points. According to him, most process theologians apply a highly selective biblical hermeneutic, welcoming Scripture when it agrees with panentheist opinion but otherwise ignoring it.[1] Moreover,

---

[1] *The Concept of God.*

process theologians often deny basic tenets of Christianity, such as the deity of Christ.[1] Schubert Ogden, for example, though referring to Christ as 'God's decisive act', holds that Christ was fully human, special only in that his words and deeds represent God's being in a normative way.[2] Also other fundamental Christian beliefs, such as the Incarnation, the bodily Resurrection and the Atonement are questioned by process thinkers.

The God of process theology fails to measure up to the omniscient, omnipotent God of the Bible. Nor, as we shall soon see, does process theology offer much hope for Christians in a life hereafter. Since the motivation for process theology was primarily that of developing a theology more in line with modern evolutionary thought, it is perhaps not surprising that this approach leaves us with little Christian content.

Life After Death

A crucial theological question is that of life after death. As Christians we set our hope on a better life in the hereafter. Does modern cosmology have anything to offer here? We saw in the previous chapter that, if we rely on purely natural processes, the fate of life in the universe is rather dismal. Can any of the gods depicted above remedy this gloomy forecast?

Fred Hoyle suspects the conviction of individual immortality to be in error. However, he does believe that our remote descendants, through immense advances in technology, would be able to guarantee the collective immortality of the human race.[3] This is, unfortunately, of little consolation to the individual, who remains a mere mortal.

Freeman Dyson and Frank Tipler are more optimistic. Dyson speculates that future technology will be able to reconstruct copies of our ancestors, if we can record the sequence of bases in their DNA cells. Perhaps, also, it may become possible to read memory traces in the ancestor's brain and to play these back. In this way it may be possible to 'resurrect' ancestors.[4]

[1] See John B. Cobb, *Christ in a Pluralistic Age,* Philadelphia: Westminster Press, 1975, p. 74.
[2] *The Reality of God and Other Essays,* New York: Harper and Row, 1966, pp. 184–6.
[3] *The Intelligent Universe,* p. 226.
[4] *Infinite in All Directions,* p. 289.

Whether this will actually work is, of course, highly doubtful. First of all, it is feasible only for those individuals for whom we have DNA samples and for whom memory traces can be recorded. But, even if complete memory traces are possible, which seems most unlikely, the corresponding technology must surely be in the far distant future, when our thoughts and brains will long since have disappeared. Past and present generations do not stand to benefit from Dyson's clever scheme. Second, even if this process were possible, it would yield only *copies* of ancestors rather than the actual ancestors. There would be no actual, conscious individual continuity or immortality.

Much the same scenario is offered by Tipler. He argues that it is possible, in principle at least, for future life to reconstruct an exceedingly accurate simulation of our past lives. Such a simulation of a living being would, according to Tipler, actually be alive:

> The simulated body could be one that is vastly improved over our present one . . . we can call the simulated, improved and undying body a 'spiritual body'.[1]

Such simulations would be made using the past light rays of our ancestors. These light rays are not lost but will be intercepted as the singularity is approached. As we near the singularity the information extracted becomes more precise. From the information extracted from this light our ancestors will be reconstructed. Even if sufficient information cannot be extracted from the past light cone, resurrection could still occur, for it would still be possible to resurrect all possible humans that could be coded in DNA, this being a finite number.

Again, this is very similar to Dyson's resurrection, except that it mentions no memory reconstruction. Much the same criticisms apply. In particular, even if it were technically feasible, this would just create a *copy* of my former self rather than being the continuation of my conscious being.

Teilhard's system, too, offers little hope for those longing for a life hereafter. When a man dies his body decomposes and turns back to ordinary, non-living matter. It follows that man's soul, being tied to his body, cannot survive as a high order of consciousness. The most that one can expect, it seems, is a great many elementary centres of consciousness, each belonging to a unit of the decomposed body,

[1] 'The Omega Point as Eschaton', p. 246.

subject to the laws of statistics. Man can survive only collectively, not individually.[1] Thus, at heart, even though Teilhard brings Christ into the picture, it is a Christ who offers us no ultimate salvation.

Regarding the destiny of man, most process theologians reject the notion of an actual heaven or hell, or any individual immortality. According to Ogden,[2] man will continue to live on only in God's cosmic memory, of which we will not be conscious. A similar position is taken by Charles Hartshorne,[3] who considers the notion of an actual heaven and hell to be a dangerous error. In process theology there is only a type of *objective* immortality: we may live on after death, but only through our past actions, only in the memory of God. There is no *subjective* immortality, in which our self continues in conscious existence.

Process theologian John Cobb, discusses the question of life after death in his book *A Christian Natural Theology*.[4] A major difficulty of the separation of body and soul, says Cobb, is where to place the soul. We no longer conceive of heaven and hell as spatial places. In Newtonian cosmology souls or mental substances fitted in so ill with the space-time continuum that it did not seem too strange to postulate another sphere, a spiritual realm, where human souls belonged. But in the evolutionary cosmos this distinction between mind and matter cannot be maintained. If minds emerged in the physical universe, then they must belong in that universe. There seems to be no longer a 'place' for the soul after death.

It is thus clear that the question of origins is closely related to that of eternal life. The supposed evolutionary origin of man undermines the ability of his soul, physically determined as it then must be, to survive death. The Dutch astronomer Herman Zanstra contends that Teilhard's rejection of the immortality of the soul does not allow for a true religion in the full sense. According to Zanstra, the chief problem for religion is whether the soul can detach itself from the body and lead an existence independent of the body without perishing. If all processes in the soul are merely a different aspect of bodily

---

[1] *The Phenomenon of Man*, p. 61.
[2] 'The Meaning of Christian Hope', *Union Seminary Quarterly Review*, 1975, 30, pp. 160–3.
[3] *The Logic of Perfection*, LaSalle, Illinois: Open Court, 1962, p. 254.
[4] Philadelphia: Westminster Press, 1965, pp. 63–70.

processes, which are entirely governed by the laws of physics, then, when the body dies, the soul will cease to exist. If the soul is necessarily tied to the body, then a past big bang and a future heat death (or Big Crunch) rule out the existence of consciousness in the distant past or far future. Such a view also has no room for God as a Spirit and is essentially atheistic. Thus Zanstra opts for dualism with interaction: soul and body are separate entities, influencing each other but yet having a certain degree of independence. His supernatural view of the world includes conscious spirits, where consciousness has existed before the physical universe began, and will continue to exist when our universe is reduced to dust and ashes.[1]

John Polkinghorne also postulates the existence of another realm, which he calls the 'noetic' world. In this world there are mental entities, such as mathematical truths, that are not anchored in the material realm, as well as spiritual entities, such as angels. Polkinghorne wants to do justice to our experience of the fact that by our 'biologically evolved consciousness we participate in a realm of reality which has not come into being either with us or with the origination of the physical world in the big bang, but which has always been there'. This noetic world may be an everlasting world but it is not an eternal, uncreated world. It does not stand alongside of God on equal terms but depends upon him. God himself is not to be found in this noetic world; he is beyond the world of his creation.[2]

Conclusions

In summary, it is evident that modern cosmology cannot easily accommodate two of the most essential ingredients for true religion: a supernatural God and subjective immortality. Clearly, to preserve these fundamental features there must be a richer reality beyond that of our observed, physical three-dimensional space. There must be a spiritual realm wherein God and the soul can exist. Such a transcendent realm is necessarily beyond the scrutiny of scientists.

Thus, ultimately, those who wish to maintain the basics of true religion must acknowledge the inadequacy of modern cosmology's depiction, not only of the future, but also of the present structure of the universe.

[1] 'Is Religion Refuted by Physics or Astronomy?', *Vistas in Astronomy*, 1968, 10, pp. 1–21.
[2] *Science and Creation*, London: SPCK, 1988, p. 76.

7

The Bible on Cosmology

What does the Bible have to say regarding cosmology? In this chapter we shall examine the biblical teaching about God, his creation, and how these are related. Of particular concern will be various specific issues relating directly to cosmology. We shall end with an assessment of big-bang cosmology as viewed in the light of Scripture.

The Being and Nature of God

First we shall summarize the biblical teaching regarding God's Being, particularly as it pertains to his creation. God is not an abstract concept or an impersonal power, but a living, personal Being who has a definite character and nature.

God as Trinity

The biblical God is a triune God. There is one God, but he exists as three distinct persons: Father, Son and Holy Spirit. The persons of the Trinity are sometimes distinguished by different functions. Thus the creation is often attributed to the Father, redemption to the Son, and sanctification to the Holy Spirit (see *Eph.* 1:3–14). Yet there exists a fundamental unity whereby all three participate in the activity of any one. For example, creation is also said to be the work of the Son (*John* 1:3) and of the Holy Spirit (*Isa.* 40:12–13).

God Is a Spirit

The Bible tell us that 'God is a Spirit' (*John* 4:24). This means, first, that God does not depend on matter: 'a spirit hath not flesh and bones' (*Luke* 24:39). God has a substantial nature all his own and distinct from the physical world. He is immaterial. He is also invisible to the bodily senses: 'the invisible God' (*Col.*1:15). The idea of spirit includes also that he is alive: 'the living God' (*Matt.* 16:16) and that he is a person, a self-conscious and self-determining Being: 'I am that I am' (*Exod.* 3:14; see also *Rom.* 9:11).

God Is Infinite

The infinity of God refers to his unboundedness: he is free from all limitations. He is in no way limited by the universe or confined to it. God is absolutely *perfect*, with no defects: 'Be ye therefore perfect, even as your Father which is in heaven is perfect' (*Matt.* 5:48). His greatness knows no bounds: 'His greatness is unsearchable' (*Psa.* 145:3). God is also perfectly wise, true, good, holy and righteous.

God's infinity is further manifested in his *eternity*, which has no bounds in time: 'From everlasting to everlasting, thou art God' (*Psa.* 90:2); and his *immensity*, which has no spatial limitations.

God Is Omnipresent

The Bible portrays God as being omnipresent. He transcends all spatial limitations and yet is present in every point in space: 'Though he be not far from every one of us: for in him we live and move and have our being' (*Acts* 17:27–28). Or, 'Can any hide himself in secret places that I shall not see him? saith the LORD. Do not I fill heaven and earth? saith the LORD' (*Jer.* 23:24).

Nevertheless, even though God is present everywhere, he does not manifest himself everywhere in the same manner. There are numerous biblical references to God dwelling particularly in a special place: 'I dwell in the high and holy place' (*Isa.* 57:15). Moreover, the place of God's particular manifestation is not fixed in time; motion is often attributed to God: the Spirit of God moved over the face of the deep (*Gen.* 1:2), God walked in the garden in the cool of the day (*Gen.* 3:8), the LORD comes to Abraham (*Gen.* 18), The LORD goes before the Israelites in a pillar of cloud (*Exod.* 13:21), the LORD comes down to Mount Sinai (*Exod.* 19:20), Moses sees God pass by (*Exod.* 33). In the Incarnation, Christ came down, from God's place, to man's place, taking on human nature; in his ascension, Christ's human, risen body goes from man's place to heaven – to a specific place – where he is now at the right hand of God (*Rom.* 8:34).

God is no spaceless or timeless abstraction, but, rather, a personal, living God who yet transcends the universe he has created.

God Is Omniscient

God's knowledge is complete and perfect. 'God . . . knoweth all things' (*1 John* 3:20). This includes all events: 'The eyes of the LORD are in every place, beholding the evil and the good' (*Prov.* 15:3). It also covers the contents of our minds and hearts: 'The LORD knoweth the thoughts of man' (*Psa.* 94:11); 'The LORD looketh on the heart' (*1 Sam.*16:7); 'The LORD searcheth all hearts, and understandeth all the imaginations of the thoughts' (*1 Chron.* 28:9).

God's knowledge encompasses also the future: 'Behold, the former things are come to pass, and new things do I declare: before they spring forth I tell you of them' (*Isa.* 42:9); 'Declaring the end from the beginning, and from ancient times the things that are not yet done, saying, My counsel shall stand, and I will do all my pleasure'(*Isa.* 46:10).

God Is Omnipotent

It is abundantly clear in the Bible that God is all-powerful: 'Whatsoever the LORD pleased, that did he in heaven, and in earth' (*Psa.* 135:6); 'With God all things are possible' (*Matt.* 19:26). 'For the Lord God omnipotent reigneth' (*Rev.* 19:6). Nothing happens by chance: 'The lot is cast into the lap; but the whole disposing thereof is of the LORD' (*Prov.* 16:33).

God is a God of order, not confusion (*1 Cor.* 14:33). He has set bounds and ordinances for his creatures (*Job* 38–41; *Jer.* 33:25). God in his infinite power and wisdom has decreed that certain regularities be maintained. He has established a law-structure for his creation. It is due only to this regular, sustaining activity of God in his creation that science is at all possible, for science could not succeed in a chaos, but only within a universe of regular patterns that can be observed, discerned, and used as a basis for predictions.

Yet God does not limit his actions to regularities: he also performs miracles. These should not be seen as divine interventions in a world that otherwise runs its own course, for God continuously upholds his creation. Rather, law and miracles should be considered as merely the regular and irregular manifestations of God's will. The main purpose of miracles is to demonstrate the almighty power of God, 'that thou mightest know that the LORD he is God; there is none else beside him' (*Deut.* 4:35). Miracles are performed not only directly by God but also through the prophets (for example, Elijah and Elisha) and Christ's disciples; as well as by angels (*John* 5:4; *Acts* 5:19) and demonic spirits (2 *Thess.* 2:9; *Rev.* 16:14).

Thus in our study of cosmology we must keep in mind that the physical universe is not a closed system of purely physical causes and effects, but that supernatural forces are also operative.

The Doctrine of Creation

The biblical doctrine of creation is aptly summarized in the *Belgic Confession* (1561):

> We believe that the Father through the Word, that is, through his Son, has created out of nothing heaven and earth and all creatures, when it seemed good to him, and that he has given to every creature its being, shape, and form, and to each its specific task and function to serve its Creator. We believe that he also continues to sustain and govern them according to his eternal providence and by his infinite power in order to serve man, to the end that man may serve his God. He also created the angels good, to be his messengers and to serve his elect (*Article* 12).

We take note of the following points:

All things were created by God

The Bible affirms that God is the Creator of everything in heaven and earth: 'In the beginning God created the heaven and the earth' (*Gen.* 1:1). Although this creation is derived from God the Father, it came about through Christ by whom 'were all things created . . . in heaven and . . . in earth, visible and invisible . . . all things were created by him and for him, and he is before all things and by him all things consist' (*Col.* 1:16–17).

Creation is a free act of the transcendent God

God is the transcendent God. He is 'above all' and 'over all' (*Rom.* 9:5), independent of his creation, self-existent and self-sufficient. He is distinct from his creation. God may not be identified with the physical universe or any portion of it. (Hence man is reproved for serving the 'creature more than the Creator' (*Rom.* 1:25) and is commanded not to worship any graven image (*Exod.* 20:4).) The creation must be understood, not as a necessary act, but as a free act of God, of God's sovereign will (see *Eph.* 1:11, *Rev.* 4:11). He did not need to create the universe (see *Acts* 17:25), but freely chose to do so.

The world is always dependent upon God

God is not only *transcendent*, but also *immanent*: he is 'through all and in all' (*Eph.* 4:6). Though distinct from his creation, God is also present in it. 'By him all things consist' (*Col.* 1:17) and 'in him we live, and move, and have our being' (*Acts* 17:28).

God is not only the Creator, the originator of the universe, but also the cause of its continuous existence: 'upholding all things by the word of his power' (*Heb.* 1:3). The universe is at all times entirely dependent upon God's sustaining power. Without God's continual upholding Word the universe would instantly cease to exist.

The purpose of the universe

God has made all things for the service of mankind, so that man in turn may use it to serve God. Man is the centre of creation; he is given dominion over it (*Gen.* 1:28). But man must exercise his dominion in a stewardly manner, serving and glorifying God. The ultimate purpose of God's work of creation is to reveal his glory: 'For I have created him for my glory' (*Isa.* 43:7).

Creation out of nothing

The explicit formulation of *creatio ex nihilo* (Latin for 'creation out of nothing') arose in the early church in reaction to the belief that matter had always existed. This challenge came in two forms: dualism and pantheism. The dualists held that God created the universe by ordering pre-existent material. Thus there were two fundamental entities: the world and God. Pantheism, on the other hand, identified God and the world, thus denying any distinct reality to the world.

In opposition to such views, the traditional Christian teaching is that the universe was created out of nothing; that is, without the use of any previous substance.

The explicit expression 'to create out of nothing' is not found in Scripture but is found in the Apocrypha (2 Maccabees 7:28). Yet this teaching seems to be confirmed by the Bible. 'In the beginning God created the heaven and the earth' (*Gen.* 1:1), implies that the physical universe had a beginning in time, being created by God. Another text often cited in support of *creatio ex nihilo* is Hebrews 11:3, 'Through faith we understand that the worlds were framed by the word of God, so that things which are seen were not made of things which do appear.' Also: 'For thou hast created all things, and for thy pleasure they are and were created' (*Rev.* 4:11). Nothing would have existed if it were not for God's will. God simply spoke and things came into existence: 'For he spake and it was done' (*Psa.* 33:9).

The doctrine of *creatio ex nihilo* is more than just an assertion of the dependence of the universe upon God for its existence: it stresses that the universe was created, at some point in time, from nothing.

Continuous Creation

In recent times many theologians have exchanged a *creatio ex nihilo* for a *creatio continua* (Latin for 'continuous creation'). Thus, for example, Barbour argues that *creatio ex nihilo*, particularly if associated with an absolute beginning, is an unbiblical concept.[1] He contends that the idea of creation 'at the beginning' is an outgrowth of ideas of the covenant and providence. Moreover, whereas *creatio ex nihilo* may fit in with the static universe of medieval cosmology, the modern universe is dynamic and evolving. It is still incomplete and in the process of being created. The coming-to-be of life from matter is seen by Barbour as being as representative of divine creation as the primeval production of matter out of nothing. Barbour merges continuing creation with providence and minimizes *creatio ex nihilo*. Ted Peters, too, even though he defends *creatio ex nihilo* against Barbour, agrees on the importance of *creatio continua*. According to Peters, God's creative work is not yet done: 'We today are still somewhere within the first six days.'[2]

Now, we must of course affirm that God continuously sustains the universe. Otherwise it would cease to exist. But the Bible speaks clearly about creation being a *past* event. At the end of the sixth day

[1] Ian G. Barbour, *Issues in Science and Religion*, New York: Harper, 1971, p. 384.
[2] Ted Peters (ed)., *Cosmos as Creation*, Nashville, Abingdon Press, 1989, p. 96.

'God saw everything that he had made, and, behold, it was very good' (*Gen.* 1:31). It was after the creation was completed that the Fall of man occurred, with the resultant curse on creation. Elsewhere, too, the six days are referred to as a *past* event: 'In six days the LORD made heaven and earth, and on the seventh day he rested, and was refreshed' (*Exod.* 31:17). Thus *creatio continua*, with its notion that the universe is still evolving upward, has no biblical support.

The History of the Universe

Creation Events

The Bible teaches that God created the cosmos out of nothing in six days. Let us briefly review the work of the first four days, as they relate to cosmological matters.

DAY ONE

In the beginning God created the heaven and the earth. And the earth was without form and void; and darkness was upon the face of the deep. And the Spirit of God moved upon the face of the waters. And God said, Let there be light: and there was light. And God saw the light, that it was good: and God divided the light from the darkness. And God called the light Day, and the darkness he called Night. And the evening and the morning were the first day (*Gen.* 1:1–5).

In the beginning God created heaven and earth. The primeval earth was a dark, structureless, chaos, largely in liquid form. As Jordan points out, nothing like this is said of heaven,[1] and the rest of the Bible indicates that heaven was structured, full, and bright from the beginning.

The creation of light was the first of three separations needed to change the chaos into a cosmos. It marked the beginning of a continuous succession of days and nights. Note that 'Day' is explicitly defined here to be a period of light.

The 'deep' or waters are said to have a 'face', or surface, implying that the initial physical universe consisted of a bounded, finite volume of matter embedded within a larger space.

Since the sun and other celestial bodies were not created until the fourth day, one might wonder what the source of light was. We are

---

[1] James B. Jordan, *Creation in Six Days: A Defense of the Traditional Reading of Genesis*, Moscow, Idaho: Canon Press, 1999, p. 174.

not told. Perhaps God created light photons directly. Douglas F. Kelly concurs with Henry Morris that the light source before the creation of the sun may well have emanated from the theophanic presence of God himself.[1] In a similar vein, Russell Humphreys suggests that the Spirit of God, moving over the surface of the waters, himself became a light source for the surface, in much the same way that he will again become a light source at a future time (*Rev.* 21:23, 22:5).[2] This gives the surface of the deep a bright side and a dark side, the movement of the light source bringing about the ensuing succession of days and nights.

DAY TWO

And God said, Let there be a firmament in the midst of the waters, and let it divide the waters from the waters. And God made the firmament and divided the waters which were under the firmament from the waters which were above the firmament: and it was so. And God called the firmament Heaven. And the evening and the morning were the second day (*Gen.* 1:6–8).

Here we have a second separation, this time a spatial one. The firmament, called Heaven, is created to separate the waters into two distinct layers, above and beneath the firmament. The firmament is generally taken to include the atmosphere surrounding the earth as well as the further portions of the sky wherein we find the sun and stars.

What, then, are we to make of the waters above the firmament? This has been the source of much speculation. Many commentators, including John Calvin, consider these waters to refer merely to clouds in the atmosphere. On the other hand, others, such as Bouw[3] and Humphreys,[4] contend that, since the sun and stars are later placed *in* the firmament, the waters *above* the firmament must be beyond the stars. Both these authors depict the universe as a huge sphere, centred on or near the earth, surrounded by a thin shell of

---

[1] Kelly, *Creation and Change*, Tain, Ross-shire: Mentor, 1997, p. 204; Morris, *The Remarkable Birth of Planet Earth*, Minneapolis, Dimension Books, 1972.

[2] *Starlight and Time*, Colorado Springs, Master Books, 1994, p. 76.

[3] Gerardus D. Bouw, *Geocentricity*, Cleveland: Association for Biblical Astronomy, 1992, p. 322.

[4] *Starlight and Time*, p. 35.

water. Whatever difficulties such a watery shell may pose for physical explanations, the positioning of this shell beyond the observational horizon at least places the problem out of sight.

Jordan argues that the waters above the firmament are in heaven itself, on the far side of the firmament.[1] He equates this water with the sea of glass, crystal, and ice that is seen in visions of heaven in Ezekiel and Revelation. He finds confirmation in Psalm 104:2–4, where we are told that God's upper chamber is built upon the waters. The firmament separates heaven and earth for the first time, placing heaven in another dimension. This barrier will be removed in the distant future, when heaven and earth are renewed, the sea is no more, and the New Jerusalem comes down from heaven (*Rev.* 21).

DAY THREE

And God said, Let the waters under the heaven be gathered together unto one place, and let dry land appear . . . And God said, Let the earth bring forth grass, the herb yielding seed, and the fruit tree . . . And the evening and the morning were the third day (*Gen.* 1:9–13).

The matter created on the first day seems to have been a confusion of undifferentiated water and mud.[2] Humphreys suggests that all the initial matter was water, some of which was transformed by God on the second day into various elements by compaction.[3] However, the Genesis text gives no indication of such transformation. The third day relates the separation of water and dry land, but no mention is made of the creation of land. Both water and the elements of the earth seem to have been created from the start, in Day One.

DAY FOUR

And God said, Let there be lights in the firmament of the heaven to divide the day from the night; and let them be for signs, and for seasons, and for days and years: and let them be lights in the firmament of the heaven to give light upon the earth: and it was so. And God made two great lights; the greater light to rule the day, and the lesser light to rule the night: he made the stars also. And God set them in the firmament of the heaven to give light upon the earth, and to rule over the day and over

---

[1] *Creation in Six Days*, p. 180.
[2] Kelly, *Creation and Change*, p. 82.
[3] *Starlight and Time*, p. 79.

the night, and to divide the light from the darkness: and God saw that it was good. And the evening and the morning were the fourth day (*Gen.* 1:14–19).

Some commentators affirm that the sun and stars were already created on the first day and that the fourth day just describes the clearing of a previously opaque atmosphere, so that the sun and stars now became visible from the earth for the first time.[1] Yet, as Kelly notes, this contradicts the text, which clearly teaches that God, on the fourth day, created celestial bodies that were not previously in existence.

As to the stated purposes of these bodies, their tasks as lights, as dividers of day and night and calculators of days, years and seasons, seem obvious enough: 'The sun to rule by day . . . the moon and stars to rule by night' (*Psa.* 136:8–9); 'He appointed the moon for seasons' (*Psa.* 104:19).

What about their functions as signs? Kelly considers the signs to include the stars' function as aids in navigation and surveying. To this one can add also that 'the heavens declare the glory of God; and the firmament sheweth his handiwork' (*Psa.* 19:1). Further, they are signs also that the Lord will do what he has promised:

And this will be a sign unto thee from the LORD, that the LORD will do this thing that he hath spoken: Behold, I will bring again the shadow of the degrees, which is gone down in the sun dial of Ahaz, ten degrees backward. So the sun returned ten degrees . . . (*Isa.* 38:7–8).

There are also celestial signs of the coming day of the Lord:

And I will shew wonders in the heavens and in the earth, blood, and fire, and pillars of smoke. The sun shall be turned into darkness and the moon into blood, before the great and the terrible day of the LORD come (*Joel* 2:30–31).

And there shall be signs in the sun, and in the moon, and in the stars (*Luke* 21:25).

But in those days, after that tribulation, the sun shall be darkened, and the moon shall not give her light, and the stars of heaven shall fall (*Mark* 13:24–25).

[1] For example, Hugh Ross, *The Genesis Question*, Colorado Springs, Navpress, 1998, p. 44.

The Fall and its Consequences

At the end of the sixth day of creation, 'God saw everything that he had made, and, behold, it was very good' (*Gen.* 1:31). Yet shortly thereafter evil entered the world. It originated in heaven with the devil – 'the devil sinneth from the beginning' (*1 John* 3:8) – who appeared on earth in the form of a serpent (*Rev.* 20:2), and enticed Adam and Eve to sin (*Gen.* 3). As a result of Adam's disobedience death entered the world and sin spread to all men.

Does the Fall have any implications for cosmology? The Bible does not make clear to what extent, if any, the stars have been affected by the Fall. On the one hand, Paul states that 'the whole creation groaneth and travaileth in pain together until now' (*Rom.* 8:22), and in the end times the celestial bodies will be transformed. On the other hand, although God specifically cursed the ground, because of Adam's sin, so that it would now bring forth thorns and thistles (*Gen.* 3:17–18), no specific mention is made of any changes to the sun, moon or stars.

Some have thought that the second law of thermodynamics was not in effect before the Fall. For example, Henry Morris writes:

> The universal validity of the second law of thermodynamics is demonstrated, but no one knows why it is true . . . But the Biblical explanation is that it is involved in the curse of God upon this world and its whole system, because of Adam's sin . . . Therefore, we conclude that the Bible teaches that, originally, there was no disorder, no decay, no aging process, no suffering, and above all, no death, in the world when the creation was completed. All was *very good*.[1]

It is hard to imagine what the universe would be like without the second law of thermodynamics. Would this imply, for example, that no frictional forces existed to slow down a ball thrown through the air? If so, how would birds fly? The physics of stars and galaxies would no doubt be greatly affected, but perhaps this is of little significance, if these objects were created full-blown, already a violation of the laws of thermodynamics, and the fall occurred very soon (a matter of days?) later.

Yet, the Fall does not seem to have brought about a huge discontinuity in the nature of the universe and its creatures. Trees still

[1] *The Twilight of Evolution*, Philadelphia: Presbyterian and Reformed, 1963, p. 37.

bring forth fruit, birds still fly and multiply, man still eats fruit and talks, and so on. Even after the Fall it was still possible for man to live forever, had he not been barred from eating of the tree of life (*Gen.* 3:22–24). All this suggests that, although the Fall profoundly affected the physical (and of course spiritual) well-being of man, the basic laws of physics were probably left intact.

Eschatology

Through the work of Christ – his incarnation, death and resurrection – salvation became possible for man. God through Christ reconciles to himself all things, whether on earth or in heaven (*Col.* 1:19–20). Now the creation is still groaning in travail, but eventually it will be set free from its bondage to decay (*Rom.* 8:19–22). At the end of this era Christ will come to judge all men and to determine their eternal destination (*Rev.* 20:11–15).

The last days will be marked by dramatic celestial signs, involving the sun, moon and stars, as noted above. After that, the first heaven and earth shall pass away and there will be a new heaven and a new earth (*Rev.* 21:1). 'For behold, I create new heavens and a new earth; and the former shall not be remembered' (*Isa.* 65:17). Then the holy city, the new Jerusalem shall come down from heaven and God shall dwell with his people for evermore (*Rev.* 21:2–3).

The apostle Peter has more to say about the destruction of the heavens:

> The heavens shall pass away with a great noise, and the elements shall melt with fervent heat, and the earth also and the works that are therein shall be burned up (*2 Pet.* 3:10).

This seems to refer primarily to heaven in the sense of atmosphere. Wilbur M. Smith speculates that the dissolving of the elements may refer to the unleashing of nuclear energy.[1] He believes that the third heaven, the abode of God, will not be affected. The old heaven and the old earth will pass away or be transformed because they are corrupted by the effects of sin, which is not true of God's abode. The earth and celestial bodies around it will not be annihilated, but only renewed to a more glorious condition.[2]

---

[1] *The Biblical Doctrine of Heaven*, Chicago: Moody Press, 1968, p. 229.
[2] *Ibid.*, p. 235.

The Date of Creation

What does the Bible say regarding the age of the world? In recent times this has been a rather contentious issue. Yet this has not always been so. Until a few hundred years ago the almost universal view of the Christian world was that the physical universe was only a few thousand years old. It was widely thought that the Bible spoke rather clearly on this: Genesis 1 told of a six-day creation, with light being created on the first day and celestial objects on the fourth day. The genealogies in Genesis 5 and 11 and other biblical data placed the creation of Adam, on the sixth day, at about 4000 BC.

The days of creation were generally regarded, by both the church fathers and, later, the Reformers, as ordinary days. Although texts such as 2 Peter 3:8 ('One day is with the Lord as a thousand years') were used to make a connection between the creation days and long periods of time, this was applied not to the creation week but to human history: many thought that the totality of history would equal six thousand years.

In the words of Davis Young, certainly no supporter of a young earth:

> It cannot be denied, in spite of frequent interpretations of Genesis 1 that departed from the rigidly literal, that the almost universal view of the Christian world until the eighteenth century was that the earth was only a few thousand years old.[1]

This consensus was challenged by geological and astronomical evidence that was viewed as demanding a much greater age for man, the earth, and the stars. Other interpretations of Genesis were then sought that were more in harmony with the new science. At first the creation days were often reinterpreted as long periods of time. Later, when even this was found to be untenable, it became popular to view the creation days as a mere literary device, a tool used to convey deeper theological truths.

It is noteworthy, however, that the proponents of the literary position often concede that, on purely exegetical grounds and excluding scientific evidence, the traditional interpretation is superior. Ramm, Blocher, Van Till and Young all explicitly state that their rejection of the literal reading of Genesis is primarily because of

[1] *Christianity and the Age of the Earth*, p. 25.

its presumed incompatibility with modern science.[1] Thus, for example, Howard Van Till asserts that 'the days of the Genesis 1 story are clearly ordinary days',[2] even though, on the basis of astronomical evidence, he can no longer accept the traditional reading of Genesis.

Nowadays the calculations of Archbishop James Ussher (1581–1656), who placed creation at 4004 BC, are often scorned. Even many Christians consider biblical chronology an acute embarrassment.

Yet the chronological nature – and completeness – of the Genesis genealogies was taken for granted by all the church fathers and Reformers. The theologians Augustine, Martin Luther, John Calvin and Abraham Kuyper all explicitly affirmed that the world was less than six thousand years old. So did scientists such as Johannes Kepler and Isaac Newton.

The chronological function of the Genesis genealogies was questioned in 1863 by William Henry Green of Princeton Theological Seminary.[3] Green made it clear that his departure from the traditional biblical chronology was motivated by his desire to harmonize the Bible with scientific conclusions regarding the antiquity of man. Consequently, he postulated that the Genesis genealogies had huge gaps, so that we are unable to date the events of Genesis 1–11. Thus we can avoid a clash with science.

However, when we read, 'And Seth lived an hundred and five years and begat Enos: and Seth lived after he begat Enos eight hundred and seven years' (*Gen.* 5:6–7), it seems clear that we have a direct father-son link. Adding up all such links, it is easy to calculate that 1,656 years elapsed from the creation of Adam to the Flood (*Gen.* 5), and a further 222 years to Terah (*Gen.* 11). The suggestion by Green that the text could be read, 'Seth lived an hundred and five years and

---

[1] Bernard Ramm, *The Christian View of Science and Scripture*, Grand Rapids: Eerdmans, 1954, p. 17; Henri Blocher, *In the Beginning*, Downers Grove: InterVarsity, 1984, p. 48; Howard Van Till, *The Fourth Day*, p. 76; Davis Young, 'Scripture in the hands of geologists', p. 295.

[2] *The Fourth Day*, p. 91.

[3] An article by Green published in *Bibliotheca Sacra*, 1890, 47, pp. 285–303, refers to an earlier paper dated 1863. The 1890 article has been reprinted as an appendix in R. C. Newman and H. J. Eckelmann, *Genesis One and the Age of the Earth*, Downers Grove: InterVarsity, 1977.

became an *ancestor* of Enos: and Seth lived after he became an *ancestor* of Enos eight hundred and seven years', seems rather artificial. Other writers have concluded that Green's arguments for gaps are spurious and that the biblical evidence favours the view that the Genesis genealogies are complete.[1]

I do not intend to enter into a detailed discussion of the exegetical specifics of the various interpretations of Genesis. For that I refer the reader to other works such as, for example, the recent study by Douglas Kelly, referred to earlier.[2] Two points that I stress are:

(1) Until recently the vast majority of Christians have adopted the traditional, literal reading of Genesis.

(2) Those who have rejected this have generally been led to do so on the basis of extra-biblical considerations. As I have argued already in Chapter 1, such a repudiation of the otherwise preferred reading of Scripture is inconsistent with the confession of the Bible as the inerrant, authoritative Word of God.

In conclusion, I take the biblical evidence to point to a creation of the physical universe about six thousand years ago. The question of whether such a young age for the universe can be worked into a viable cosmological model will be addressed in the next chapter, when we investigate various creationist cosmologies.

The Spiritual Realm

God has created not only the physical universe, but also a spiritual world. In recent years relatively little has been written about heaven and the spiritual realm. Modern science, particularly cosmology, has cast doubt upon the existence of heaven. Yet the Bible speaks very clearly about a spiritual world. Moreover, since the spiritual world interacts with the physical, this has profound implications for cosmology.

Angels

The heavenly realm is the dwelling place not only of God, who is a Spirit (*John* 4:24), but also of angels. The task of angels is to worship

---

[1] Richard Niessen, 'A biblical approach to dating the earth: a case for the use of Genesis 5 and 11 as an exact chronology', *Creation Research Society Quarterly*, 1982, *19*, pp. 60–6; C. G. Ozanne, *The First Seven Thousand Years: A Study in Bible Chronology*, New York: Exposition Press, 1970.

[2] *Creation and Change.*

God (*Rev.* 4), to execute God's will (*Psa.* 103:20), and to minister to believers (*Heb.* 1:14).

The angels have not always existed but were created: 'Praise ye him, all his angels . . . for he commanded, and they were created' (*Psa.* 148:2, 5). Apparently their creation took place before the earth was made – 'Where wast thou when I laid the foundations of the earth . . . when all the morning stars sang together, and all the sons of God shouted for joy?' (*Job* 38:4,7) – but during the creation week (*Gen.* 1:1; 2:1).

These spiritual beings are normally invisible, 'for a spirit hath not flesh and bones' (*Luke* 24:39). Angels are part of the invisible creation referred to in Colossians 1:16. Yet God sometimes opens our eyes to them, as in the case of Elisha and his servant (*2 Kings* 6:17). At other times they take on bodily form (*Gen.* 19, *Judg.* 13, *Luke* 1). Angels can communicate with God (*Job* 1:6), with man, and with each other (*Rev.* 7:2). Their activity can have physical effects, such as the slaying of the Assyrians (*2 Kings* 19:35) and the blinding of the Sodomites (*Gen.* 19:11).

Angels were originally created holy and were endowed with free will. Some, under the leadership of Satan, rebelled against God (*Rev.* 12:7–10). Satan has been defeated by the life, death, and resurrection of Christ but this defeat will not be complete until the end of this age. Meanwhile Satan and his spiritual forces continue to tempt believers and to struggle against God's plans.

Heaven

In the Bible the word 'heaven' has various meanings. The first heaven is the atmosphere and is no doubt meant in such passages as *Gen.* 7:11 and 11:4. The second heaven refers to the celestial sky, filled with planets, stars, and galaxies.

Then there is the third heaven, to which Paul was caught up (*2 Cor.* 12:2) and which he also called 'paradise'. This is the dwelling place of God (*Psa.*11:4) and of his angels (*Mark* 13:32). It is also the ultimate destination of all believers, who look forward to 'an inheritance incorruptible, and undefiled, and that fadeth not away, reserved in heaven for you' (*1 Pet.* 1:4). The redeemed will be resurrected with spiritual rather than physical bodies (*1 Cor.* 15:44). This spiritual body will have the qualities of incorruptibility, glory, power, and immortality (*1 Cor.* 15:42–44). Our resurrected bodies will be like that of Christ (*Phil.* 3:21). The resurrected Christ had a body in some ways like our natural bodies, yet in other ways quite different. He could be seen and touched, he could eat food, and yet he could also appear and disappear suddenly. The risen Christ could conform to the physical world as he chose, much as other spiritual beings such as angels can. The spiritual body is thus greater than the physical body, including it, but also transcending it.

What happens between death and resurrection? Where does the soul reside? The traditional Christian position has been that at death the soul immediately returns to God (see, for example, *Eccles.*12:7, *Luke* 23:43, *Acts* 7:59). The souls of the righteous are received in heaven, where they behold the face of God and await the full redemption of their bodies; the souls of the wicked are cast into hell, there to await the day of judgment. A detailed defence of the traditional view of the bodiless existence of the soul from death to resurrection has been made by John Cooper in his book *Body, Soul, and Life Everlasting.*[1]

Heaven and Space

How is God's place related to man's place? The Bible makes it clear that the physical and spiritual worlds are not isolated but are closely connected.

The spiritual realm is no mere abstraction but has a concrete spatial aspect. The biblical description suggests that the spiritual heaven is a universe parallel to the physical universe. Although heaven is normally invisible to man, it is at times *opened* (see, for example, *Ezek.*1:1, *Mark* 1:10, *2 Kings* 6:17) so that man may catch a glimpse of heavenly things: 'Ye shall see heaven open, and the angels of God ascending and descending upon the Son of man' (*John* 1:51).

We are told of Michael and his angels fighting in heaven against Satan and his angels, who were defeated, 'neither was their place found any more in heaven' (*Rev.* 12:7–8). Angels, even as spirits, occupy a place in heaven and can be displaced. Christ ascended up from Jerusalem into the sky, was taken into heaven, where he now sits at the right hand of God, and will return in the same manner. The

[1] Grand Rapids: Eerdmans, 1989.

heavenly visions of John picture God seated on a throne surrounded by angels, elders, and saints. Again, we are given a spatial image. Revelation 21 tells us of the new Jerusalem coming down from God's heaven to earth: in the future heaven, God's place, and man's place will be one. The new Jerusalem is depicted, not as a transformed earthly city, but as one that originates in heaven and is suspended over the earth. As such it seems to be, not *non*-spatial but, rather, *super*-spatial, transcending our three-dimensional physical space.

In light of these considerations, several authors have speculated that perhaps the physical and spiritual worlds should be considered to be in some sense parts of a higher, multi-dimensional space. This idea will be investigated further in the next chapter.

Heaven and Time

Heaven is not a timeless place. Events take place in a time sequence: there is a 'before' and 'after'. Angels are created, some rebel and are later ejected; at particular times angels present themselves before the Lord (*Job* 2:1); Christ in his human, though risen, body and the souls of the departed enter heaven; in heaven there are temporal acts such as prayer, speech, singing, harp playing (*Rev.* 5:8–12), and even half an hour of silence (*Rev.* 8:1). In fact, heavenly and earthly time appear to be closely correlated: they both appear to be synchronized to the same divine clock. Okke Jager , in an extensive study on time and eternity, concludes that, in the Bible, earth-time, hell-time, and heaven-time are all one.[1]

What about time in the future heaven, as the redeemed enter into God's eternity? It appears that this future is eternal in the sense of being endless, or everlasting, rather than timeless. This is evident from the description of the New Jerusalem:

> Then he shewed me a pure river of water of life . . . proceeding out of the throne of God . . . and on either side of the river, was there the tree of life, which bare twelve manner of fruits, and yielded its fruit every month . . . They shall see his face, and his name shall be in their foreheads. And there shall be no night there; and they need no candle, neither light of the sun, for the Lord God giveth them light: and they shall reign for ever and ever (*Rev.* 22:1–5).

[1] *Het Eeuwige Leven: Met Name in Verband met de Verhouding van Tijd en Eeuwigheid,* Kampen: Kok, 1962, p. 511.

The flowing water, the act of reigning (forever!), the fruits ripening each month all point to acts within time. While there is clearly much symbolism in Revelation, there is nowhere any contrary suggestion of our future eternity as being timeless rather than endless.

Time and Eternity

How is God's eternity related to time? Should it be related to time everlasting or to timelessness?

The question of the relationship between time and eternity is a perplexing one. As finite, time-bound creatures, we have great difficulty conceiving of infinity and timelessness. How can we, fallible human beings as we are, presume to describe the attributes of God? We must therefore be cautious, avoid idle conjectures and consider what God has revealed to us about himself regarding time and eternity.

The Bible never portrays God as a passive, timeless abstraction. On the contrary, he is always described as an active agent in history. God is the *living* God (*1 Tim.* 4:10), who acts in time. Moreover, God exists throughout time everlasting, without beginning or end:

> Before the mountains were brought forth, or ever thou hadst formed the earth and the world, even from everlasting to everlasting, thou art God. (*Psa.* 90:2).
>
> Thy years shall have no end (*Psa.* 102:27; compare *Heb.* 1:12).

This implies that time itself extends infinitely far into both the past and future. The reference to 'before' the foundation of the earth entails that time existed before the creation of physical things. Hence the creation of the physical world can be seen as a temporal act of God.

The *Belgic Confession*, speaks of God creating heaven and earth 'when it seemed good to him' (*Article* 12). This implies that creation was not *with* time, as some have asserted, but within a pre-existing time. Also, in discussing the two natures of Christ, the *Belgic Confession* (*Article* 19) contrasts Christ's human nature, which is created and has a beginning of days, with Christ's divine nature, which is 'without beginning of days or end of life'. The underlying thought is one of eternity as boundless time.

John Calvin (*Institutes*, I. xiv. 1) replies to the 'profane jeer' that it seems strange that it did not occur to God to create heaven and earth sooner, rather than allow an infinite period to pass before doing so, by pointing out the futility of speculating on things that God has purposely concealed.

God's eternity involves also his ability to perceive all of time simultaneously. He knows the past and future as perfectly as he does the present. His 'present' fills all of time. We, on the other hand, experience a succession of events. Our 'present' is at most a few seconds; our limited past is recalled only imperfectly; our future is to us as yet unknown.

Furthermore, the Bible tells us that God, though active in history, is immutable. He does not change in his Being, perfections, purposes and promises. His knowledge, moral principles and volitions remain forever the same.[1] This is seen in such texts as:

> For I am the LORD, I change not; therefore ye sons of Jacob are not consumed (*Mal.* 3:6).

> But thou art the same, and thy years shall have no end (*Psa.* 102: 27).

Berkhof notes that God's *immutability* does not imply *immobility*, for God is always in action. Rather, divine immutability signifies that God's interactions with his creation are always consistent with his most perfect character and always faithful to his merciful promises.

In summary, the biblical evidence favours the view that time extends infinitely far into both the past and future, from everlasting to everlasting. God's eternity is supra-temporal, encompassing boundless time. Also, God's perception and experience of time is quite different from ours. He has full knowledge of all past, present and future events, which are to him as one seamless whole. Finally, God's activity throughout time is always marked by the immutability of his Being and his promises.

Further Cosmological Questions

We shall next examine a few further questions of cosmological and astronomical significance.

The Stars as Signs

Do the stars serve as signs in other capacities than those discussed above? A number of authors have thought so.

---

[1] See Louis Berkhof, *Systematic Theology,* London: Banner of Truth, 1958 (frequently reprinted), pp. 58–9.

The Gospel in the Stars

Several writers have asserted that the grouping of stars into constellations depicts a divine message – the history of salvation – written in the sky.[1] They note that, although Adam named the animals, God himself named the stars: 'He telleth the number of the stars; he calleth them all by their names' (*Psa.* 147:4; see also *Isa.* 40:26). They believe that these names are still preserved in the constellations and the story they tell. As to the story told by the stars, Fleming refers to Psalm 19:

> The heavens declare the glory of God; and the firmament sheweth his handiwork. Day unto day uttereth speech, and night unto night sheweth knowledge. There is no speech nor language, where their voice is not heard. Their line is gone through all the earth, and their words to the end of the world.

The fact that the latter part of this passage is quoted in Romans 10:18 with clear reference to the preaching of Christ is taken by Fleming to mean that the constellations present the gospel message.

This is quite an intriguing thesis. Yet one wonders how viable it is. Are we to believe that this celestial message, conveying man's fall and salvation, was already in place and observed by Adam before his actual Fall? Or did God re-arrange or rename the stars after the Fall? Either option seems implausible.

A further difficulty is that the patterns of the stars themselves usually have little resemblance to the corresponding constellations, even when allowing for motions of the stars and extrapolating the shapes of the constellations back to the time of Paul or David. For example, it is evident that the stars in the constellation *Ara* are not readily discerned to form the figure of an altar, nor do the stars in *Virgo* clearly reveal a woman (see *Figures* 7.1 and 7.2). Once the stars are assigned to the various constellations the association can be made but this requires a *verbal* explanation along with our observation of the stars. The question may thus be asked, why God, who placed the stars in the sky, did not arrange them in more obvious patterns, if their purpose was to present the gospel message.

---

[1] See J. A. Seiss, *The Gospel in the Stars,* 1882, repr. Grand Rapids: Kregel, 1972, and K. C. Fleming, *God's Voice in the Stars, Zodiac Signs and Gospel Truth,* Neptune, N.J.: Loizeau Brothers, 1981.

Furthermore, the need for verbal explanation weakens the above references to Psalm 19 and Romans 10.

It is well known that the figures and names of the constellations do have an ancient history, dating back to at least the Sumerians and Akkadians, the non-Semitic inhabitants of the Euphrates valley prior to the Babylonians, before 2000 BC. Job, one of the oldest books of the Bible, seems to refer to several constellations:

> Canst thou bind the sweet influences of Pleiades, or loose the bands of Orion? Canst thou bring forth Mazzaroth in his season? or canst thou guide Arcturus with his sons? (*Job* 38:31–32).

The word Mazzaroth is thought by many to refer to the twelve zodiacal signs (the constellations along the apparent path of the sun). Unfortunately, there is no consensus as to the meaning of the ancient star names or the constellations.

Astronomer Michael Ovenden, by deducing the position of the North Pole in ancient pictures of the constellations, traces the origin of the constellations to about 2600 BC. Although not a Christian, he concludes, regarding a portion of the constellations (see *Figs.* 7.1,2):

> Coming from the ship (*Argo*) is the *Centaur*, a man-animal, sacrificing a Beast (*Lupus*) upon an altar (*Ara*). We see, too, the Water-snake (*Hydra*) with a Raven (*Corvus*) eating its flesh. There can be no doubt that here we have, in imagination pictured in the sky, a version of the story of Noah and the Flood. The picture is complete with the Milky Way seeming to rise as smoke from the Altar.[1]

Although this sounds promising, this interpretation of these constellations is quite different from that of Fleming, who interprets, for example, the *Centaur* as Christ, the man-God, *Lupus* as Christ, the slain victim, and *Ara* as the lake of fire prepared for the Devil.

Thus, although the naming of the constellations is undoubtedly of ancient origin, and very likely related to biblical themes, it is evident that their original meanings have been corrupted. The initial message, even if it were of divine origin, is not easily recovered.

The Star of Bethlehem
One might ask: If Paul did refer to such a clear gospel in the stars,

---

[1] M. W. Ovenden, 'The Origin of the Constellations', *Philosophical Journal*, 1966, 3, pp. 1–18.

why do no other writers from Paul's day mention it? Yet, there may perhaps be a further indication that the constellations do convey a deeper message. Consider the story of the star of Bethlehem. When the magi come to Jerusalem they ask, 'Where is he that is born King of the Jews? for we have seen his star' (*Matt.* 2:2). How did they know that the star signified the birth of the King of the Jews? There is no evidence that they had received any direct revelation of this. Rather, it seems that they deduced the birth of a new, important Jewish king purely from celestial signs. In that case they must have attached meanings to celestial events that had at least some degree of truth in them.

There has been much speculation about the identity of the star of Bethlehem. The three most popular naturalistic explanations have been that of a comet, a supernova, or a conjunction of the planets Jupiter and Saturn. However, none of these proposals do justice to the reported behaviour of the star:

> When they had heard the king, they departed; and lo, the star, which they saw in the east, went before them, till it came and stood over where the young child was. When they saw the star, they rejoiced with exceeding great joy (*Matt.* 2:9–10).

Note the peculiar motion of the star during the short journey of the magi from Jerusalem to Bethlehem: first leading, then stopping over the right place. The exceeding great joy of the magi when they saw the star further implies its unusual behaviour, either by its sudden reappearance or by its altered motion. Clearly, had the star been leading them all along, they would not have had to ask for directions in Jerusalem. No comet, supernova, or combination of planets would exhibit such strange behaviour.

Yet, while the star itself probably was supernatural, its initial position among the constellations may have had high significance. But where would that be? Fleming thinks it may well have been a new star in the constellation *Coma*, near *Virgo*; he interprets *Coma* to mean 'the desired son' of *Virgo* (the virgin). According to Colin Humphreys,[1] in Magian astrology the planet Saturn represented the divine father, Jupiter his son, and the constellation *Pisces* was

[1] C. J. Humphreys, 'The Star of Bethlehem – a Comet in 5 BC – and the Date of the Birth of Christ', *Quarterly Journal of the Royal Astronomical Society*, 1991, 32, pp. 389–407.

Figure 7.1: Constellations of the Northern Sky.
From Sir W. Peck, *The Observer's Atlas of the Heavens.*

Figure 7.2: Constellations of the Southern Sky.
From Sir W. Peck, *The Observer's Atlas of the Heavens.*

associated with Israel. Hence the conjunction of Saturn and Jupiter in *Pisces* in 7 BC would generate the astrological message that a Messiah-King would be born in Israel.

On the other hand, Ernest Martin identifies the star of Bethlehem with Jupiter, the king planet, entering the constellation *Leo*, associated in the Bible with the tribe of Judah, from which Jesus came, on 12 August in 3 BC. At that time the sun, representing the supreme father, was positioned near Venus, the mother, and had just entered the constellation *Virgo*, the virgin.[1]

The preference for *Leo*, the Lion, is based on Balaam's prophecy, 'There shall come a Star out of Jacob' (*Num.* 24:17), combined with Jacob's blessing, 'Judah is a lion's whelp' (*Gen.* 49:9).

Clearly, much of this is pure conjecture. One suspects that, with a little ingenuity, a case could be made for almost any constellation. Thus, while there was undoubtedly some significance to the initial place of appearance of the star within the constellations, we can no more than guess as to either the initial position or its significance.

The Size of the Universe

Could the physical universe be infinitely large? Most Christian theologians have favoured a finite creation. Many have believed that only God can be unlimited or infinite and that any physical theory asserting the universe to be infinite in time or space should thus be ruled out on religious grounds. Norman Geisler, for example, argues that it is impossible to have two infinite beings, for infinity includes all and there cannot be two 'alls'. Thus there can only be one infinite Being – God – and all other things must be finite. He finds finiteness to be an essential property of creation.[2]

On the other hand, Don De Young speculates that perhaps there is an actually infinite number of stars – 'What an excellent way for the Creator to show his glory!'[3]

Let me note first that I do not find Geisler's argument convincing. Certainly, one must grant that there can be no other Being who is infinite in the full sense in which this is attributed to God, with all its

---

[1] E. L. Martin, *The Birth of Christ Recalculated,* Pasadena: Foundation for Biblical Research, 1980.

[2] *Knowing the Truth about Creation,* Ann Arbor: Servant Books, 1989, p. 9.

[3] *Astronomy and the Bible,* Grand Rapids: Baker Book House, 1989, p. 57.

connotations of perfection and unboundedness. It is not clear to me, however, that this necessarily rules out the existence of entities that embody a limited form of infinity. For example, if God exists everlastingly in time, then both God and time are infinite, in the sense of temporal unboundedness. This involves no contradiction. Could not the same apply also to God and space, that God and space are both unlimited? Furthermore, to the extent that God's spiritual space transcends man's three-dimensional space, even an infinite physical three-dimensional universe might still be merely a small sub-space of a much larger multi-dimensional space.

Are there any biblical indications that our physical world is infinite in space? Texts such as, 'As the host of heaven cannot be numbered, neither the sand of the sea measured: so will I multiply the seed of David' (*Jer.* 33:22), though referring to stars 'without number', clearly mean this only in the sense of 'very large', too large for man to count, since the sand and the seed are both finite.

Biblical texts such as, 'He telleth the number of the stars; he calleth them all by their names' (*Psa.* 147:4), seem to point to a finite number, for how can an infinite number of stars all have names? Moreover, the purpose of the stars was to give light upon the earth, and for signs and seasons (*Gen.* 1:14–18). This suggests that, to fulfil this mandate, no star can be infinitely far away.

Finally, as we noted above, the fact that the 'deep' in Genesis 1 has a surface implies that, at least on the first day, the material universe was finite, bounded within a larger space. Presumably, the matter would still be finite and bounded after the creation of the firmament and separation of waters on the second day, though this does depend somewhat on how 'firmament' is interpreted, particularly when stars are placed in the firmament on the fourth day.

On the whole, I conclude that the biblical evidence tends to favour a finite physical universe, perhaps embedded in infinite space. Of course, in practice, this question is largely academic, since observationally we can never distinguish between a universe merely larger than the observed portion and one that is infinitely large.

An Expanded Universe?

According to Humphreys, the firmament has expanded. In support of this he points to numerous texts that speak of the stretching out of the heavens: He 'hath stretched out the heavens' (*Jer.* 10:12, see also *Job* 9:8, *Psa.* 104:2, *Isa.* 40:22). The expansion began, says Humphreys, on the second day, when the firmament was created. The second day is the only day when God did not comment that it was good. Yet on the sixth day God declared all things he had made 'very good' (*Gen.* 1:31). Humphreys suggests that God did not declare the second day good because the expansion was not completed on the second day, but lasted until, or shortly before, the sixth day.[1]

It is quite plausible that at the end of the second day the material universe was larger than it had been the previous day, since now the firmament had been added to separate the waters that had previously been mixed together. In that sense the universe may be said to have expanded. On the other hand, at that time there were not yet any celestial objects.

Was there a further expansion after the second day? Since the sun and stars were not created until the fourth day, only that portion of the expansion from the fourth to the sixth day would be cosmologically pertinent. Humphreys' argument from the lack of a 'very good' on the second day is rather tenuous. Further, why should the completion of the expansion be signified by the 'very good' of day six rather than the 'good' of day four, when the celestial objects in the firmament are created? After all, after day four the creation account mentions only the creation of earthly, living creatures.

The more usual interpretation of the stretching out of the heavens is that this refers to their initial creation, on the second day, rather than to their subsequent expansion. Any proposed further expansion after the second day is pure speculation.

The Biblical Frame of Reference

The frame of reference of the Bible is clearly geocentric. Events are measured with respect to their position relative to the earth (see *Josh.* 10:12–14). The earth can be held to be fixed also in a deeper sense: the earth is said to be at rest with respect to the heavenly dwelling-place of God (see *Isa.* 66:1), who establishes all absolutes. This is certainly the case in the life-to-come, when the new Jerusalem will come down from heaven and the dwelling of God will be with man (*Rev.* 21:2–3).

---

[1] *Starlight and Time,* p. 68.

The question may be asked whether such geocentricity has any scientific significance. As we noted in our earlier discussion of Galileo and the Church, only relative motion is observable. Absolute motion is meaningless unless we define the standard with respect to which 'absolute' motion is to be measured. There is nothing objectionable in considering earth – or heaven – as the absolute standard of rest. It may not be the most convenient definition, from a purely scientific point of view, but it can hardly be considered false. The choice of an absolute standard is primarily a philosophical matter, rather than a scientific one. Thus one cannot fault the Bible for applying a geocentric framework. One may prefer some other point of reference, but one cannot conclude that the Bible has erred.

Biblical geocentricity defines the earth's rest with respect to heaven, God's throne, which is unobservable to man (unless God chooses to open our eyes). As such it has obvious theological implications but few, if any, physical ones.

Is the universe geocentric also in the sense that the earth is at or near the geometric centre of the universe? The creation account in Genesis 1 places the earth at the centre, surrounded by the waters under the firmament, the firmament, and the waters above the firmament. Humphreys[1] speculates that during the creation week the earth was at or near the centre of a spherical universe. However, the Bible itself specifies no particular shape of the universe. Nor, for that matter, does it indicate that stars and galaxies are distributed with spherical symmetry about the earth.

It must therefore be stressed that biblical geocentricity need not imply that the earth is at the exact geometric centre of the solar system, the galaxy, or the universe. Nor does geocentricity imply that a geocentric dynamics would be more convenient than, say, Newtonian or relativistic mechanics.

In conclusion, it seems to me that biblical geocentricity has no direct, necessary, observational or scientific implications. Yet it does point beyond the physical world of our observations to the richer, hidden, spiritual reality of heaven.

The Big Bang and the Bible
Many Christians have eagerly embraced big-bang cosmology. Thus,

[1] *Ibid.*, p. 71.

for example, evangelical theologian Norman Geisler exclaims, 'The big bang theory is in amazing accord with the creation account of Genesis 1:1',[1] and astronomer Hugh Ross goes so far as to assert that the Bible 'is the only religious text that teaches a cosmology in full agreement with the latest astrophysical discoveries'.[2] Fred Heeren, in a similar vein, echoes, 'The Bible is the only religious source coming to us from ancient times that fits the modern cosmological picture'.[3]

Are such claims justified? Should, and can, big-bang cosmology be reconciled with the Bible?

In an earlier chapter we have already noted various weaknesses of big-bang cosmology, the subjectivity of cosmological theorizing, and the possibility of constructing alternative cosmological models. We have cautioned against equating big-bang cosmology with revealed truth. Hence, from this perspective, it is not essential that the Bible be in accord with big-bang cosmology.

Nevertheless, the question may be asked, to what extent is there agreement between Scripture and the big-bang model?

The Big Bang and the Past

It is clear that the big bang and Genesis do have a number of things in common. For example, both depict the universe as originating at a finite time in the past, with light one of the first things to be created and man the last, at least up to now (if life is a result of evolution it can be expected to eventually produce beings more advanced than man).

Yet there are also obvious differences. For one, the billions of years demanded by big-bang cosmology greatly exceed the six creation days of Genesis 1. Treating the days as long periods of time is of little help since the days are defined as periods of light and darkness.

Secondly, the order of creation differs significantly. The main discrepancy, no doubt, concerns the creation of the sun and stars. But there are further differences that are problematic. In evolutionary scenarios the oceans are formed after the dry land. Davis Young, in his critique of concordism, contends that, according to evolutionary

---

[1] *Journal of the Evangelical Theological Society,* 1979, 22, p. 282.
[2] *The Fingerprint of God,* p. 179.
[3] *Show Me God: What the Message from Space Is Telling Us about God,* Wheeling: Searchlight, 1995, p. xvii.

geology, marine life preceded land vegetation. Also, in the evolutionary view, land animals and birds preceded fruit trees.[1] Such considerations yield the following sequences:

Big Bang	*Genesis 1*
1. light, light elements	1. water, earthly elements (Day 1)
2. stars	2. light
3. heavy elements, water	3. firmament, oceans, atmosphere (Day 2)
4. sun, moon, earth	4. dry land (Day 3)
5. dry land	5. land vegetation, fruit trees
6. oceans	6. sun, moon, stars (Day 4)
7. marine life	7. marine life (Day 5)
8. land vegetation	8. birds
9. land animals: reptiles	9. land animals (Day 6)
10. birds	10. man
11. land animals: mammals	11. woman
12. fruit trees, grasses	
13. humans	

Thirdly, there is the mode of creation. In Genesis everything is created seemingly instantaneously by God. He spoke and it was. In the big bang everything arises gradually through evolutionary processes, based solely on the operation of natural laws.

Fourthly, according to Genesis the creation, including man, was initially 'good', but was later spoiled by the Fall, which put a curse on creation. According to the big-bang evolutionary picture, man did not fall, but rose and is still evolving upwards. It is particularly this notion of man's original goodness and subsequent Fall that is difficult to fit into a naturalistic view of origins.

The Big Bang and the Future

A reconciliation between the big bang and Genesis, even if that were exegetically sound, would still not give the big bang a clean bill of theological health. Other problems remain. Consider, for example, questions regarding the future.

[1] 'Scripture in the hands of geologists', p. 293, 287.

As we saw in an earlier chapter, big-bang cosmology implies a gloomy outlook for the future: continued evolution is bound to replace man with more intelligent beings, but eventually all life is doomed to extinction in either a Big Crunch or a heat death. There are no physical grounds for believing in a personal life hereafter.

Obviously, this picture of the future has little in common with that of the Bible. The central hope of Christianity is that of the return of Christ, the resurrection of the dead, the last judgment, and life everlasting in a renewed heaven and earth. And these events are to occur soon, not billions of years in the future.

The Big Bang and Spiritual Reality

Finally, the big-bang theory raises problems for Christianity, not only in its description of the past and future, but, even more importantly, in its conception of the present structure of the universe. It assumes that the physical universe is all that exists; only physical causes and effects influence our universe. There is thus no place for a transcendent God, for supernatural causes, or for an immortal soul. At death man's life is forever extinguished.

The Bible, in contrast, points to the existence of a spiritual realm wherein are found God, angels, and the souls of the departed. The biblical heaven seems to be a universe parallel to our physical world, but usually invisible to man. Modern man makes the mistake of considering the physical world to be the ultimate reality, with the spiritual world as little more than an idle abstraction. In actuality, however, it is our physical three-dimensional cosmos that is no more than a thin, fleeting shadow: the ultimate reality is the multi-dimensional abode of God.

Implications

Christians attempting to reconcile big-bang cosmology with the Bible generally limit this to matters pertaining to origins. By acknowledging biblical eschatology, as well as the existence of spiritual and supernatural elements in the world, they have already abandoned major portions of big-bang cosmology.

The Bible gives few specifics regarding the origin of astronomical objects. Therefore, with regard to astronomy, it may seem fairly easy to bring Genesis in line with big-bang cosmology. Only the nature, length and order of the creation days need then be adjusted.

Although such apparently minor modifications may seem rather harmless, there is more at stake than first meets the eye.

First, such a forcing of the biblical text reflects an epistemology that gives more weight to scientific theorizing than to God's Word. Those who advocate concordance between Genesis and big-bang cosmology often adhere to a double-revelation theory. Hugh Ross, for example, argues that

> the facts of nature may be likened to a sixty-seventh book of the Bible . . . we can expect interpretations of the facts of nature to be consistent with the message of Genesis.[1]

His mistake is to extend the content of such facts beyond observational data to include also specific scientific theories, such as big-bang cosmology. The limitations of general revelation were discussed in Chapter 4. Let me repeat here that scientific theories, particularly regarding origins, are highly speculative, subjective, unverifiable and constantly changing. By no means can they be given the status of divine truth. Observational data, by contrast, stand on much firmer ground. They can be considered as essentially factual. However, in cosmology, these data consist primarily of light photons as they reach our eye or telescope. Such observations are limited to (some) events in the present and recent past. We have no direct observations of the distant, pre-historic past. Hence we have no genuine scientific facts about origins. All scientists can do is speculate.

What is really at stake, then, is nothing less than the authority and interpretation of God's Word. If humanistic thinking is to dictate our reading of Genesis 1, then we have surrendered the basic principle that worldly wisdom is to be judged in the light of Scripture, rather than *vice versa*. If we cannot believe the Bible in all that it says, even in seemingly minor matters, how can we believe it in anything it says?

Second, the acceptance of an old universe and, by implication, an old earth, requires more than a mere rewrite of Genesis 1. According to evolutionary geology, human-like fossils can be dated back 4.5 million years. How is this to be reconciled with the biblical Adam? As Marvin Lubenow points out, neither an ancient Adam nor a

---

[1] *Creation and Time,* Colorado Springs: Navpress, 1994, p. 56.

recent Adam can easily be harmonized with an old earth.[1] An ancient Adam involves stretching the genealogies of Genesis 5 and 11 to implausible lengths. Also, the depiction of Adam as an intelligent farmer (see Genesis 4) contradicts the evolutionary notion of early man as a dim-witted cave-dweller, a hunter and gatherer who lived long before the appearance of domesticated animals and grains. On the other hand, placing Adam only a few thousand years ago raises the problem of what to do with the human look-alikes that existed before Adam, and how to account for their death, which should have been a result of Adam's fall. In short, the biblical Adam cannot plausibly be placed within the framework of evolutionary chronology. The denial of the biblical Adam, in turn, undercuts the historicity of the Fall and the reality of original sin. This has major theological implications.

Hence, this issue is much more important than may appear at first sight. As history has shown, failure to uphold literal creation days, in opposition to naturalistic science, undermines the defence of the rest of Scripture.

Conclusions

In summary, we have discussed a number of biblical teachings about the nature of God and creation. We shall enumerate some of the main conclusions.

The Bible tells us very little about the present physical structure of the universe. Its message is much more concerned with the relationship of the created cosmos to its Maker. As such it informs us of the divine plan for the universe. Everything was created, from nothing, in six days, a few thousand years ago. The original creation was good but, through Adam's fall, sin entered the world. Man's salvation is based on the incarnation, death and resurrection of Christ. On the last day Christ will return to judge the world and to bring in new heavens and a new earth in which sin will have no place.

Of great significance is the existence of a spiritual realm, which points to a larger reality beyond our limited three-dimensional physical world. The main feature of a Christian cosmology must be a proper recognition of the spiritual world, with its possible interactions with our physical universe.

[1] *Bones of Contention*, Grand Rapids, Baker, 1992.

A number of further cosmological questions have been addressed. Biblical evidence suggests that the physical universe is finite. Evidence for a gospel in the stars and the case for an expanded universe are doubtful. Although the Bible uses a geocentric frame of reference, this has no necessary observational or scientific consequences.

Finally, the relation between big-bang cosmology and the Bible has been discussed. We found that they clashed, not only regarding origins, but also regarding eschatology and the existence of spiritual entities. Embracing big-bang cosmology has major implications, far beyond a mere revamping of Genesis 1.

8

Biblical Cosmologies

In the previous chapter we found that big-bang cosmology is not easy to reconcile with Scripture. Is it possible – and desirable – to construct cosmological models that are more in accord with the Bible? These questions will be the focus of this chapter.

As we noted before, the Bible has little to say regarding the present physical structure of the universe. It does not conflict with any current astronomical *observations*. Problems arise once we move from observation to theory. The observed cosmological data available to us can be interpreted in a number of different ways; modern cosmology offers a great variety of models purporting to explain the astronomical observations. Our assessment and choice of cosmological models have more to do with prior philosophical and religious biases than with pure observation and deductive logic. A Christian approach should therefore insist that scientific theories be constructed to be consistent with biblical data.

The biblical input to cosmology is concerned primarily with matters of origins, the spiritual realm, and the future. As to the future, since heaven and earth will be renewed via supernatural means, there will be only a limited natural continuity between this age and the next. Hence it is impossible to construct an adequate cosmological model for the distant future. All that can be said is that any model for the present physical universe can be valid for at most a limited time – until Christ returns. Also the spiritual realm, and its relation to the physical world, are beyond scientific investigation. Again, we can construct no concrete cosmological model, nor establish any pertinent mathematical relations. However, the existence of spiritual causes of natural effects does set another limit on the adequacy of cosmological models.

This leaves us primarily with the problem of explaining current astronomical observations in terms of biblical givens concerning origins. In recent years a number of attempts have been made to construct cosmological models that are in harmony with the Bible. We shall refer to these as 'biblical cosmologies', recognizing that, although they may be based on particular biblical data, their specifics necessarily require additional assumptions.

We shall examine two classes of cosmologies. The first class consists of cosmological models constructed within the constraints of biblical chronology; the second class of models is concerned more with spatial, rather than temporal, considerations.

Young Universes

Creationists have concentrated on models consistent with a very young age: some six thousand or so years. The difficulty they face is that of explaining those features of the universe that are usually taken to indicate ages of billions of years. For example, if the universe is six thousand years old, how is it that we can see galaxies that appear to be billions of light years away? If the distant galaxies are billions of light years away must their light not have travelled for billions of years to reach us?

Various solutions to this problem have been proposed. Let us briefly examine them.

1. A Variable Speed of Light

Barry Setterfield has proposed that the speed of light was infinite at creation (at about 4000 BC) and has decreased since then to its present value. Hence the light from distant galaxies, travelling at a phenomenal speed, could reach us in a very short time.[1] A similar model,

---

[1] 'The Velocity of Light and the Age of the Universe', *Ex Nihilo*, 1981, *4*, No.1, pp. 38–48, and No.3, pp. 56–81.

worked out in more detail but without specifying a short age for the universe, has been proposed by the Russian physicist V. S. Troitskii.[1] In these models the reduction in the speed of light effectively causes a decrease in the observed frequency, so that light from distant galaxies appears red-shifted. Thus the model yields also an alternative to expansion as an explanation of the red shifts. Indeed, Setterfield suggests that the universe is presently in a state of contraction, whereas Troitskii advocates a static universe. Troitskii's model also generates the observed characteristics of the background radiation.

These models have further interesting features. Assuming, among other things, the stability of atoms and the observed constancy of the hydrogen spectrum from distant stars, a change in the speed of light requires corresponding changes in a number of other fundamental physical 'constants'. One implication of great geological significance is that the decay rates of radio-active substances would also be much greater in the past. This could explain why radio-dates of rocks give such large apparent ages.

Is there direct observational evidence for a reduction in the speed of light? The speed of light was first measured in 1675. Norman and Setterfield have extensively analysed historical measurements and have claimed to demonstrate an exponential decay.[2] Their analysis has, however, been questioned, particularly with regard to the values of a number of crucial historical determinations. Furthermore, over the last few decades, when very sensitive measuring devices are available, the decay seems to have stopped. Thus the empirical evidence is, at present, inconclusive.

Even if a change in the speed of light could be observationally demonstrated, it is quite another matter to extrapolate this exponentially far beyond the direct observational data, as Setterfield has done. The hypothesis that the speed of light was virtually infinite six millennia ago must surely be regarded as much more speculative than the mere notion of a variable speed of light. Nevertheless, such speculations are not easy to disprove.

Yet, even if Setterfield's theory were valid and could account for our observation of distant galaxies in a young universe, it yields no

[1] 'Physical Constants and Evolution of the Universe', referred to on p. 52.
[2] Trevor Norman and Barry Setterfield, *The Atomic Constants, Light and Time*, Flinders University, Australia, 1987.

naturalistic explanation of the formation of these galaxies. Biblical chronology is measured in terms of solar years, a time unit dependent upon the strength of gravity. All time-variations must therefore be compared to that of gravity. Now, the time for the formation of planets, stars, galaxies and other large-scale structures from an initial cloud of gas depends largely on the strength of the gravitational constant. Since this must be considered invariable (as it actually is by both Setterfield and Troitskii), we end up with very large formation times for these celestial objects, if we posit purely physical processes. It follows that, in Setterfield's cosmology, it is still necessary to postulate that stars and galaxies were created in mature form as full-blown objects.

Other variations on Setterfield's theme are possible. For example, perhaps the speed of light varies with position in space, rather than with time. One could conjecture that the speed of light is larger at large distances from the earth, approaching infinity at the edge of the universe. Or perhaps the speed of light is somehow dependent upon the gravitational field. In interstellar space, where gravity is small, the speed of light could be very great; close to stars it might be close to the speed measured near the earth. No doubt a mathematical relation could be concocted that would yield suitably small light travel times while still satisfying all the observational constraints.

Such hypotheses would, however, have less explanatory power than Setterfield's theory, for they would not affect radio-dating on earth. Hence, even more than in Setterfield's model, they would have to be supplemented with some form of mature creation.

One difficulty with theories of this nature is that they are largely *ad hoc*, introduced solely to save a cherished idea seriously threatened by unfavourable evidence. There is very little in the way of supporting evidence for such strange behaviour of light. There is no obvious physical reason why the speed of light should depend on position or time. On other hand, the mere fact that a theory is *ad hoc* is not sufficient to disprove it. Moreover, as we saw in earlier chapters, such *ad hoc* theorizing is very common in cosmology. In fact, as noted in a previous chapter, the notion of a time-varying speed of light has recently been employed by Albrecht and Magueijo and John Barrow,[1] to solve a number of pressing problems associated with big-bang

[1] See p. 65.

cosmology. They, too, postulate that the speed of light was initially virtually infinite, at the big-bang singularity. It seems that, at least in this regard, creationist cosmology is in no worse shape than big-bang cosmology.

2. Time Dilation

Another possibility is that clocks on earth tick slower than elsewhere in the universe. This effect is known as *time dilation*. According to the theory of general relativity, the rate at which a clock ticks depends on the motion of the clock and on the local gravitational field. Is it possible that time dilation caused light from distant galaxies to travel billions of light years during, say, only a few earth years?

One method of inducing time dilation is through expansion. Distant galaxies moving away from us at high speeds would have their light shifted to the red end of the spectrum. This corresponds to an apparent slowing down of clocks on the galaxies. As the galactic recession speed approaches the speed of light the galactic clocks come to a full stop.

Unfortunately, such time dilation is exactly opposite to what is required. It is the *earth* clock, rather than the *galactic* clocks, that should be slowed down. Both Peacock[1] and Schroeder[2] suggest that the six creation days are to be measured in terms of a divine clock, moving at close to the speed of light, rather than in terms of an earth clock. Many billions of earth years could then have passed during the corresponding six days of divine time. But this will not do. The days of Genesis are clearly defined as periods of light and darkness as measured on the *earth*. Thus the time dilation due to expansion just makes things worse.

A more sophisticated hypothesis has recently been advanced by Russell Humphreys.[3] He has developed a rather elaborate cosmological model wherein the universe is considered to have emerged from a 'white hole', the opposite of a collapse into a black hole. The main idea is that an earth-based observer is near the centre of a finite,

[1] Roy E. Peacock, *A Brief History of Eternity*, Wheaton: Crossway Books, 1990, p. 111.
[2] G. L. Schroeder, *Genesis and the Big Bang*, New York: Bantam Books, 1990, p. 53.
[3] *Starlight and Time*.

bounded universe. In such a universe the gravitational field is strongest at the centre. Hence we would experience a slower clock rate than galaxies far from the centre.

Although this model has received a fair amount of publicity, Humphreys' scenario is highly speculative and he has not yet backed it up by definite quantitative calculations. In most general relativistic cosmologies significant time dilation does not occur. Indeed, it has been shown that even in Humphreys' model there is no time dilation, contrary to Humphreys' claims.[1] Although it is possible to concoct particular models that do have a sufficiently large time dilation, the huge time dilation required causes other, unwanted, observational effects. The prime difficulty is that such time dilation models predict either large galactic blue shifts or very large red shifts that decrease with distance. This is contrary to what is actually observed. At this time it is not clear how this shortcoming can be resolved.

Furthermore, this model, too, does not eliminate the need for mature creation. Presumably time dilation might allow distant stars sufficient time to develop via natural means. However, this would not be the case for nearby stars. Certainly not for the sun, where the cosmic gravitational potential, and hence the clock rate, is essentially the same as at the earth.

3. Curved-Space Models

Another possibility concerns the determination of galactic distances. Is the universe really billions of light years (using the speed of light as measured near the earth) in size? Distances to stars and galaxies are estimated on the basis of the assumption that space is, at least approximately, the 'flat' space of normal, Euclidean geometry. Flat space is characterized by the usual features of Euclidean geometry, such as the rule that the inner angles of a triangle add up to exactly 180 degrees.

What if space is not flat, but 'curved'? In a curved (also called 'non-Euclidean') space, the inner angles of a triangle do not add up to 180 degrees. There are two types of curved spaces: 'spherical' and 'hyperbolic'. In a spherical space the angles of a triangle add up to more than 180 degrees (as happens when you draw a triangle on a

---

[1] See John Byl, 'On Time Dilation in Cosmology', *Creation Research Society Quarterly*, 1997, *34*, pp. 26–32.

spherical orange); in a hyperbolic space the sum is less than 180 degrees. If space is actually curved then distance estimates assuming flat space could be seriously off the mark.

Some time ago Moon and Spencer developed a curved-space model of the universe wherein the light-travel time to distant objects was taken to be at most 15.7 years.[1] Although this model has since been cited by numerous creationists, it has a number of serious deficiencies. For one, it postulates that the curved space applies only to light; material objects still behave as if space were flat. This seems very strange. One might expect that the universe is either flat or curved, but certainly not both simultaneously. Furthermore, even if this flaw could be remedied, this model does not solve the creationist's problem: the curved space it proposes is a *spherical* space, which will make distant objects appear *closer*, rather than *further away*. This will tend to make the universe seem smaller − not larger − than it actually is (see *Figure* 8.1).

This can all be resolved, however, by assuming space to be hyperbolic. Such a space will, due to the bending of light rays, make close objects appear to be far away (*Figure* 8.1). In this way the entire universe, apparently billions of light-years in size on the assumption of flat space, can be fitted into a sphere of a few thousand light years.[2] For nearby stars there will be no significant observable difference between this model and flat space. The distinction does become substantial for distant galaxies which, as might be expected, will be drastically flattened in the direction of the line-of-sight.

It is clear that this model suffers from the same drawbacks as the ones in the previous section. It is largely *ad hoc*. Also, while it can account for the fact that we can see apparently distant objects in a young universe, it cannot account for their origin. Again, it must be postulated that stars and galaxies were created as full-blown, mature entities.

4. Mature Creation

It seems, then, that it is difficult for a creationist cosmology to avoid at least some degree of mature creation. It must generally be

[1] P. Moon and D. E. Spencer, 'Binary Stars and the Velocity of Light', *Journal of the Optical Society of America*, 1953, *43*, pp. 635–41.
[2] John Byl, 'On Small Curved-Space Models of the Universe', *Creation Research Society Quarterly*, 1988, *25*, pp. 138–40.

(a)

(b)

Figure 8.1: The Effect of Curved Space on Apparent Distances.

Part (a) shows the effect of the positive curvature of spherical space. Part (b) shows the effect of the negative curvature of hyperbolic space. The solid rays refer to the actual light rays; the grey curves refer to the apparent paths, assuming light travels in straight lines. Note that spherical space tends to decrease the apparent distance, whereas hyperbolic space increases it.

assumed, for example, that stars were not formed via a long natural process, but were created virtually instantaneously in a miraculous fashion.

A star created as a unit would have its various parts in appropriate gravitational, thermal, and radiative relationships, otherwise the star could not remain stable. Light at the surface of a star would not have originated from the interior of the star, as would be assumed by theories of stellar evolution. Rather, such light would have been created at the surface, 'en route', and could be interpreted to have an apparent prior history.

Similar considerations apply to an entire galaxy created as a unit in mature form. It would be created complete with all its constituent parts: stars and gas, their gravitational fields, and light radiation (photons). Both the light photons and gravitational effects would be have been created 'en route', but apparently originating from stars.

The same reasoning could be applied to clusters of galaxies and even larger systems that seem to be in gravitational interaction. In a young universe, with insufficient time for gravity to act, they would have had to be created as a unit, complete with their internal gravitational interactions. If gravity moves at the speed of light, as assumed by general relativity, then creating large astronomical objects with gravitational fields in place seems equivalent to creating light photons 'en route'.

But structures of galaxies can be huge, covering a sizeable fraction of the universe. It is thus but a small step to extend the notion of mature creation to the entire universe. Could not the whole astronomical cosmos have been created as a full-blown unit, complete, not only with stars and galaxies in gravitational interaction, but also with photons of light created at the same instant as the stars from which they are apparently derived, as suggested by John C. Whitcomb and Henry Morris?[1] In that case speculative theories of variable light speeds and curved spaces can be dispensed with.

Mature creation, radical as it may seem, does have a number of distinct points in its favour. Since it refers to the past, no present or future observations or experiments can refute it. Nor is it contrary to reason, there being nothing illogical about such an origin of the universe. Thus it is beyond both observational and logical disproof.

[1] *The Genesis Flood,* Philadelphia: Presbyterian and Reformed, 1961, p. 369.

Cosmologist George Ellis notes:

A modern cosmologist who was also a theologian with strict fundamen-
talist views could construct a universe model which began 6000 years
ago in time and whose edge was at a distance of 6000 light years from
the solar system. A benevolent God could easily arrange the creation of
the universe . . . so that suitable radiation was travelling toward us from
the edge of the universe to give the illusion of a vastly older and larger
expanding universe. It would be impossible for any other scientist on
the Earth to refute this world picture experimentally or observationally;
all that he could do would be to disagree with the author's cosmological
premises.[1]

Another physicist, Herbert Dingle, writes of mature creation:

There is no question that the theory is free from self-contradiction and
is consistent with all the facts of experience we have to explain; it certainly does not multiply hypotheses beyond necessity since it invokes
only one; and it is evidently beyond future refutation. If, then, we are to
ask of our concepts nothing more than that they shall correlate our
present experience economically, we must accept it in preference to any
other. Nevertheless, it is doubtful if a single person does so.[2]

Any objections – and many have objected – must therefore be
based upon deeper philosophical and theological considerations. Let
us examine some of the more prominent criticisms that have been
raised.

a. It is not testable

One might object that such theories are untestable, and hence not
scientific. To this it might be replied that untestable theories might
still be true, that other theories in big-bang cosmology are equally
untestable, and that, after all, untestability is an arbitrary criterion of
what qualifies as 'scientific'.

Even so, physicist Frank Tipler has shown that it is possible to
construct falsifiable creationist models:

It is universally thought that it is impossible to construct a falsifiable
theory which is consistent with the thousands of observations indicating an age of billions of years, but which holds that the Universe is only

---

[1] 'Cosmology and Verifiability', p. 246 (cited on p. 57).
[2] 'Philosophical Aspects of Cosmology', *Vistas in Astronomy*, 1960, *1*, p. 166.

a few thousand years old. I consider such a view to be a slur on the ingenuity of theoretical physicists: we can construct a falsifiable theory with any characteristics you care to name.[1]

In Tipler's model it is assumed that the density was so great six thousand years ago that it is impossible to extrapolate the laws of physics beyond this point in time. The density is caused by the explosion of numerous small black holes. Tipler claims to be able to explain all the current observations, as well as making some specific predictions regarding future, more detailed observations (for example, concerning the spectrum of gamma radiation).

The basic thrust of his model is that, while the universe may appear to be very old, this is just an illusion. He notes that such an illusory history is not unique to his theory. The many-worlds interpretation of quantum mechanics requires that, due to the observed interference of probability amplitudes, there are in reality many alternative histories that give rise to the present. Tipler writes:

> For example, although it is generally agreed that Julius Caesar existed, there is also a history leading to the present in which he did not exist. The Many Worlds Interpretation asserts that both histories actually occurred and both combined to give rise to us.[2]

Tipler notes that he does not really believe his creationist theory; it was developed to challenge cosmologists and philosophers to give good reasons for rejecting it on scientific grounds. Tipler claims that his theory satisfies not only falsifiability, but most other criteria discussed in the scientific literature.

b. A five-minute-old universe

A second objection to the concept of mature creation is that one could in a similar fashion argue that the entire universe, along with our memories of an apparent past, was created five minutes ago. And thus, if we allow such reasoning, we have no guarantee that any part of our history is real.[3]

---

[1] 'How to construct a falsifiable theory in which the universe came into being several thousand years ago', *Proceedings of the 1984 Biennial Meeting of the Philosophy of Science Association, Vol. 2,* Lansing, Michigan: The Association, pp. 873–902.   [2] *Ibid.,* p. 891.

[3] See, for example, Clarence Menninga, 'Creation, time and 'apparent age' ', *Perspectives on Science and Christian Faith,* 1988, 40, p. 161.

To this it can be responded that the case for a six-thousand-year-old universe, as opposed to one five minutes old, is based on more than just a philosophical possibility. To its proponents it is grounded upon the explicit testimony of God, as revealed in the Bible. According to E. H. Andrews:

> The Bible testifies for a mature creation some thousands of years ago, and thus limits our freedom to employ *reductio ad absurdum* arguments to the concept of mature creation.[1]

Andrews bases this claim on the traditional, literal reading of Genesis.

c. No room for process

A further concern that has been raised is that the creation account itself speaks of the universe as being formed over a six-day span and involving work, rather than being created instantaneously. To answer this objection Andrews develops the theory of 'miraculous process'. Mature creation refers to the end product after the six-day creation. God may well have made use of special processes. Consider, for example, the Genesis account of the creation of Adam and Eve. It is clear, however, that such processes were not the sole product of the usual natural laws. Particularly the creation of Adam and Eve demonstrates that their formation, while perhaps not quite instantaneous, was still of a most miraculous nature.[2]

d. Divine deception

The main objection against a mature creation is that it implies deception on the part of God. Thus, for example, Van Till writes:

> One cannot deny the antiquity of any celestial object without at the same time denying the authenticity of the entire history of events that are revealed by the object's properties . . . the question is whether the physical record of the object's history is authentic or merely an elaborately detailed fiction.[3]

This difficulty becomes particularly acute when mature creation includes the light apparently coming directly from distant objects. If

---

[1] *In* O. R. Barclay (ed.), *Creation and Evolution: When Christians Disagree,* Downers Grove, Illinois: InterVarsity Press, 1985, p. 164.   [2] *Ibid.*, p. 65.
[3] *The Fourth Day*, p. 171.

the light from distant objects is created *en route*, then it will never actually have come from those objects. Thus any information about events that we may infer from this light will be pure illusion. Indeed, it could be that the galaxies do not even exist, just their light. Changes in light intensity might correspond to supernova explosions that never actually took place. To quote van Till again:

> All but the last few thousand years of a multibillion-year cosmic history would be no more than an illusion . . . a divinely perpetrated hoax.[1]

How valid is this charge? Andrews argues that God can hardly be charged with deception if mature creation is revealed in Scripture. Man may ignore the Bible and thus come to false conclusions about the age of the universe. But then he has only himself to blame. Even if man is misled by the evidence because he insists upon a rigidly naturalistic explanation of origins, it does not follow that God intended to mislead or deceive.

Andrews notes that God does at times hide the truth from the 'wise and prudent' while revealing it to 'babes' (*Matt.* 11:25). The fault, however, should be attributed to those whose minds are blinded rather than to God. In a similar vein, Roy Clouser, in discussing the nature of God, remarks:

> Scripture does say that God cannot lie (*Titus* 1:2, *Heb.* 6:18), but these remarks occur in an explicitly covenantal context meaning that he cannot lie to believers because he has promised not to. It should be borne in mind that at other loci Scripture specifically says that God deceives those who are not believers (*Ezek.*14:9, 2 *Thess.* 2:11).[2]

The last text in this quote affirms that God sends a strong delusion upon those who reject the truth, to make them believe that which is false.

Also, it should be noted that an apparent age and history of an object are not properties intrinsic to that object. Rather they can be inferred only on the basis of the theoretical model that is used to interpret the observed characteristics. The illusion of a particular past history arises only when we view the data through the mirror of a particular set of theoretical premises. Since different models may

---

[1] *The Fourth Day,* p. 239.
[2] *The Myth of Religious Neutrality,* Notre Dame, Indiana: University of Notre Dame, 1991, p. 309.

yield various apparent histories, the choice as to which to prefer depends on our criteria for theory selection. It is always possible to construct models that interpret the observational data in a manner consistent with the traditional biblical chronology.

It must be kept in mind that, as pointed out above, if the creation of light (or gravity) *en route* is ruled out on the grounds that God is not deceptive, this applies equally to the instantaneous creation of mature clusters of galaxies, single galaxies, and even stars. All these objects, being of finite size, would apparently have needed a period of time for all the gravitational and radiative interactions to form properly functioning wholes. Instantaneous creation would necessarily have created fictitious past histories for gravitation and light.

Van Till's approach is based on the assumption of purely natural, time-invariant physical causes. This in essence denies the ability of God to perform miracles. Scientists always strive to explain presently observed characteristics of an object in terms of a closed chain of postulated past natural causes and effects. Hence any such scientific analysis, when applied to miraculous events, must yield erroneous results. Consequently, any miraculous event could, by the above reasoning, be classified as deceptive. It is interesting to note, by the way, that the miraculous wine at the wedding at Cana did result in a deceived governor who wondered why the best wine was kept for last (*John* 2:10). Are we to conclude from this that Jesus was deceptive?

Surely God is not being deceptive when he uses supernatural powers; he is free to act as he pleases. On the contrary, the limitation we are faced with here is one of human reasoning rather than one of divine action. God can be said to be deceiving us only if he has given divine approval to our theoretical assumptions. Since this is hardly the case, one could better contend that the evolutionary view of the past must be wrong, else God is deceiving us in his revealed Word.

Summary

In conclusion, while it is clear that various creationist cosmologies can be constructed, it must be acknowledged that most of these models are rather *ad hoc*, have not been worked out in much detail, and often have few distinctive observational implications. As such they are unlikely to convince sceptics.

Almost all creationist models ultimately draw upon the concept of mature creation. While this notion may be logically, observationally, and theologically unassailable, it does have one notable scientific deficiency. It offers very little in the way of detailed explanations for specific features of astronomical observations, other than affirming that that is just how God made things. In that sense big-bang cosmology, with all its shortcomings, at least attempts to develop a coherent explanation of many observational features.

Ultimately, however, the essential question must be that of the reliability of a cosmological model, rather than of broad, but illusory, explanatory powers. Our final goal is not the mere construction of detailed explanatory theories that satisfy the subjective criteria determining what is 'scientific', but, rather, a realistic depiction of past history. The bottom line is that creationist cosmologies, despite their weaknesses, are in harmony with divinely revealed facts, whereas big–bang cosmology is not.

Geometric Models

A number of biblical cosmologies have been more concerned with the geometry of the universe than with its age. While none of these has been worked out in detail, we very briefly list a few here for the sake of interest and completeness.

Geocentric Models

A number of cosmologies place the earth at or near the geometric centre of the universe. This, as we saw, is consistent with biblical givens, but not necessarily demanded by them. It is consistent also with the observed isotropy of the universe and, as such, is a viable alternative to the cosmological principle, which assumes the universe is everywhere the same. Bounded, spherically symmetric universes, centered on the earth (or at least our galaxy) have been presented by Ellis, Rao and Annapurna, Humphreys, and Gentry.[1]

It must be pointed out, however, that these models are, strictly speaking, not geocentric. The earth is not placed at the centre of the solar system, nor at the centre of the galaxy. The centre of the universe is generally taken to be a point near our galaxy but, observationally, the centre cannot be determined precisely. Furthermore, these models all consider the earth to be moving with respect to the centre of the universe.

[1] See references cited on pp. 52 and 160.

A variety of more genuinely geocentric models take the universe to be rotating about a fixed earth. Lynden-Bell has shown that, in general relativity, the universe rotating about a fixed earth would produce Coriolis and centrifugal forces, the bulge at the earth's equator, and all other phenomena generally adduced to prove that the earth is rotating.[1] A common objection to geocentricity is that this would make the galaxies revolve about the earth at speeds greater than that of light. In general relativity, however, an object is constrained to move at a speed less than that of light only with respect to the background space, which in turn may move at a speed greater than that of light. In the geocentric model the background space itself, with all the galaxies embedded in it, is revolving about the earth and thus the objection does not apply. Hence, according to general relativity, a geocentric universe is quite viable.

Non-relativistic geocentric models have been developed by Moon and Spencer[2] and Barbour and Bertotti.[3] None of these authors claims to be Christian.

A geocentric model in an explicitly biblical framework has been constructed by Gerardus Bouw.[4] He considers the firmament, created on the second day and extending throughout the universe, to be an extremely massive structure having a huge density of 10^{93} gm/cc. One cubic centimetre of this firmament would have much more mass than the entire observable physical universe! According to Bouw, the firmament has a natural rotational period, due to the presence of the matter within it, of one day. In its rotation it carries with it all the stars and galaxies embedded in it. This model, with its detailed depiction of the firmament, is clearly highly speculative and much further work remains to be done.

In this age most people, including Christians, believe geocentricism to be obviously contrary to fact. Yet the basic thesis is in fact notoriously difficult, if not impossible, to disprove. Supposed disproofs tend to be rather simplistic, ignorant of the above general relativistic results and missing the deeper problems regarding absolute motion.

[1] 'Mach's Principle from the Relativistic Constraint Equations.' See also p. 32.
[2] See p. 195.
[3] J. B. Barbour and B. Bertotti, 'Gravity and Inertia in a Machian Framework', *Il Nuovo Cimento*, 1977, *B38*, pp. 1–28.
[4] *Geocentricity* (see also p. 160).

Thus, for example, Martin Selbrede quite handily defends geo-centricity against the criticisms of Gary North.[1]

On the other hand, adherents of geocentricity go too far when they claim that geocentricity can be scientifically proven. As we have seen, at heart this is not a scientific question at all.

The Inverted Universe

A rather unusual model of the universe has been advocated by Fritz Braun. From his interpretation of biblical texts he concludes that the earth should be inverted: the earth's surface is the *inside* of a hollow sphere enclosing the sun, moon, and stars. Heaven is at the centre of the inverted universe, thus making this model literally theocentric (see *Figure* 8.2).[2]

A similar hollow-earth theory was advocated in the 1870s by the American cult leader Cyrus Teed, and in the 1930s in Germany. The latest promoter is Mostafa Abdelkader, from Alexandria, Egypt.[3]

At first sight this model seems obviously false. For example, if it were true then one might think that we should be able to see across the hollow sphere to the other side of the earth. In 1933, in Magdeburg, Germany, promoters of the hollow-earth theory wanted to prove their theory by means of a rocket. They reasoned that if a rocket, fired straight up, were to crash on the opposite side of the earth, then proof would be established. As Willy Ley relates, various rockets were fired but, unfortunately, they all malfunctioned and the test was eventually abandoned.[4]

However, this model is not that easily dispensed with. In practice it is frustratingly difficult to disprove. In fact, the theory can be devised so that disproof is impossible.

The above tests assume that the normal laws of physics hold and that, in particular, light travels in roughly straight lines and rockets remain a constant size. But what if this is no longer the case?

The hollow-earth model can be derived from the more usual picture of the universe via a simple mathematical transformation

[1] 'Geocentricity's Critics Refuse to Do Their Homework', *Chalcedon Report,* 1994, No. 351, p. 239.

[2] *Das Drei-Stockige Weltall der Bibel,* Salem-Obw.: Morgenland Verlag, 1973.

[3] 'A Geocosmos: Mapping Outer Space into a Hollow Earth', *Speculations in Science and Cosmology,* 1983, 6, pp. 81–9.

[4] *Rockets, Missiles and Space Travel,* New York: Viking Press, 1951.

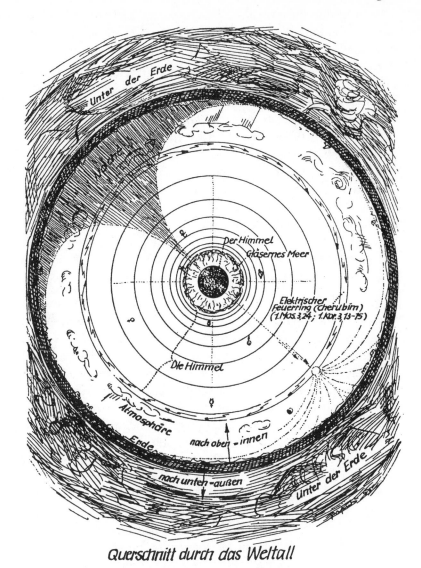

Querschnitt durch das Weltall

Figure 8.2: The Inverted Universe.
From Fritz Braun, *Das Drei-Stockige Weltall der Bibel* (also published in English as *Space and the Universe*). Note that heaven is placed at the centre, surrounded by the glassy sea, planets, the sun and clouds. Note also the curved light paths.

called a 'geometric inversion'. The procedure is very simple. For each point in the universe, measure its distance r from the centre of the earth and move the point along the centre-to-point line to a new distance $1/r$. The result of this operation is that all objects originally outside the earth (mountains, houses, clouds and stars) are now inside, and *vice versa*. The laws of physics are also inverted, with consequences that may seem strange for those accustomed to thinking in terms of the more conventional universe. For example, light now travels in curves. Also, a rocket launched from the earth to outer – or, rather, now 'inner' – space will shrink and slow down as it approaches the central heaven, never quite reaching it.

Consequently, Braun's inverted universe is observationally indistinguishable from the more conventional models of the universe. Yet, although the two models are empirically identical, they reflect quite different ways of viewing reality, particularly, in Braun's case, regarding spiritual entities and theological concerns.

The Multi-Dimensional Universe

In the previous chapter we noted the spatial aspect of heaven. How is the space of heaven related to the space of our physical world? An interesting position has been developed by the Dutch theologian Luco Van den Brom. He suggests that God exists spatially in his own more-dimensional universe. If God has existed from everlasting, and if God is spirit, then God's place, the spiritual world, must have always existed. In his act of creation God made room for the three-dimensional physical world in his higher-dimensional world. Van den Brom views the ascension of Christ as the withdrawal of Christ's body from the three-dimensional created world into the higher-dimensional system of heaven.[1]

In this way it is possible to speak of God's heaven as a place outside of our space without having to consider heaven as a place in an unreal sense. We could consider heaven as having more than three dimensions, or as being a three-dimensional world parallel to our own in a four-dimensional space, much like two two-dimensional planes embedded in a three-dimensional space. In a more recent work Van den Brom suggests that, because of the logic of Anselm's conception that God must be thought of as 'a being than which

[1] *God Alomtegenwoordig*, Kampen: Kok, 1982.

nothing greater can be conceived', divine space must possess an infinite number of dimensions.[1]

In such a space it is also natural that our physical world could be influenced by factors outside of it. The higher-dimensional world of God could have its own laws, which would hold alongside of the laws of our three-dimensional world. These higher laws and dimensions are not open to scientific research. Hence physical effects caused by higher-dimensional beings would have no natural (that is, physical) explanation and would be interpreted as miraculous. Further conse-quences of a higher-dimensional space have been drawn. Hugh Ross, for example, considers the miraculous appearance of the risen Christ in a locked a room (*John* 20:19). How could a being with a physical body (see *Luke* 24:37–43) pass through walls? Ross contends:

> Jesus would have no problem doing this in His extra dimensions. Six spatial dimensions would be adequate. He could simultaneously trans-late the first dimension of His physicality into the fourth dimension, the second into the fifth, and the third into the sixth. Then He could pass through the walls of the room and transfer His three-dimensional body from the fourth, fifth, and sixth dimensions back into the first, second, and third.[2]

Later, Ross refers to the well-known analogy of two-dimensional beings ('flatlanders') living on a flat plane. Such imaginary creatures were invented by Edwin A. Abbott who gave an entertaining descrip-tion of what life might be like in a two-dimensional universe in his book *Flatland*.[3] Flatlanders could experience only two-dimensional objects on the plane, and hence would have conceptions of length and width, but not of height. They would not be able to enter a closed square drawn on the plane, whereas a three-dimensional being could do so simply by moving up, in the third dimension, and thus stepping over the boundary without disturbing it. In a similar manner one could conceive of a multi-dimensional being entering a three-dimensional enclosure. However, following the Flatland anal-ogy, it would seem that only one additional spatial dimension is needed, rather than the three extra dimensions described by Ross.

[1] 'Interpreting the Doctrine of Creation', in Vincent Brummer (ed.), *Interpreting the Universe as Creation,* Kampen: Kok Pharos, 1991.
[2] *The Creator and the Cosmos,* Colorado Springs, Navpress, 1993, p. 73.
[3] *Flatland,* 1884, repr. New York: Dover, 1992.

Ross contends that various other theological concepts can be clarified using multi-dimensional space. For example, flatlanders would not be able to see a large three-dimensional object positioned just above them. Yet this object, though invisible, could be nearer to each of them than they are to each other. Likewise, a multi-dimensional being could be near to all of us and yet invisible. Further, Ross asserts that in multi-dimensional space the concept of the Trinity becomes mathematically feasible.

Imagine that a three-dimensional being pokes his finger through the plane of the flatlanders. The flatlanders would view this as the miraculous appearance of a circle. If the same being were to poke three fingers through Flatland, then the flatlanders would observe three distinct two-dimensional objects. In the same manner God's multi-dimensional unity could generate an apparent plurality in three-dimensional space. Elsewhere, Ross makes the dramatic claim:

> All the paradoxical doctrines in the Bible (e.g. the Trinity, free-will and predestination, eternal security, baptism in the Holy Spirit, heaven, hell, spiritual gifts) can be resolved and understood within the context of extra-dimensional reality.[2]

In his later book *Beyond the Cosmos* Ross elaborates upon this thesis.[3] Yet, William Craig, in his review of Ross, finds that, for most of the listed 'paradoxes', Ross's resolutions have little to do with extra-dimensionality. Further, Craig finds many philosophical and theological shortcomings in Ross's explanations.[4]

Although I endorse the notion of the spatiality of heaven, and of a reality beyond our three physical dimensions, it is evident that a few words of caution are in order. First, it must be kept in mind that any higher dimensions are qualitatively different from the three observed physical dimensions. In the higher dimensions physical laws, such as the limited speed of light, may not apply or, if they do, may take on quite different forms. As Van den Brom notes:

---

[1] *The Creator and the Cosmos*, p. 148–9.
[2] *The Fingerprint of God*, p. 183.
[3] *Beyond the Cosmos*, Colorado Springs, Navpress, 1996.
[4] 'Hugh Ross's Extra-Dimensional Deity: A Review Article', *Journal of the Evangelical Theological Society*, 1999, 42, pp. 293–304.

God's world is not this created world writ large: although we use the same concept of space in the model of God's higher dimensional agency, that does not imply that the content of the space of the creatures is the same as that of the divine space with the same natural laws and the same fundamental constants.[1]

The higher dimensions should certainly not be confused with the extra-spatial dimensions required by superstring theories in physics.

Second, it follows that we must be careful regarding speculations about God. As finite humans we are in no position to fully understand God. Certainly in this life we are constrained to look through a glass darkly; our knowledge of the spiritual realm is very limited, being confined to what God has revealed to us. Although some of the above examples may perhaps illustrate how some theological concepts can be better illustrated in multi-dimensional space, this should underline, not the adequacy of our conception of the spiritual realm, but, rather, the limitations of our normal three-dimensional outlook.

Again, as with the other geometric models, there are no observational characteristics that would enable us to confirm (or disprove) this kind of model scientifically.

Summary

All of these geometric models point to a larger reality beyond that of the physically-observed universe. Their main feature is the affirmation of theological truths, particularly the existence of a spiritual realm. Yet these models, to the extent that they are observationally indistinguishable from the more usual way of viewing the universe, offer us little in the way of distinct predictions for physical cosmology.

Limits of Biblical Cosmology

What is the proper function of a biblical cosmology? As we have already noted, they are important as models of reality, as reflections of theological truths. Through such models we can demonstrate various possibilities of combining observational data with biblical insights. It is worthwhile to show that the Bible and astronomical observations are not at odds with each other.

[1] 'Interpreting the Doctrine of Creation.'

Cosmology and Apologetics

But can they do more than that? Many Christians are not content with merely constructing alternative cosmologies. They would like to prove that a biblical cosmology is somehow 'better', in some widely-accepted, scientific sense, than the secular models. It is hoped that through demonstrations of the superiority of a biblical cosmology one may attain the apologetic goal of convincing the unbeliever of the truthfulness of the Bible.

Of course, models involving a mature creation or an invisible heaven can hardly be expected to serve such an apologetic function. For that it is necessary to devise a more detailed model that makes specific observational predictions. Perhaps something along the line of a detailed theory for a changing speed of light or a novel system of geocentric mechanics. At present such theories might still be inadequate, facing various theoretical and observational shortcomings. But that need not deter us. A hefty investment of research funding and talent is bound to resolve many of the current difficulties.

Yet it must be asked whether the diligent development of elaborate theories is a worthwhile expenditure of the limited resources of the Christian community. To what extent can such cosmological models be used for apologetic purposes?

There are dangers involved with staking too much on a particular scientific model. First, the more elaborate the model, the more susceptible it is to observational disproof. While it can always be patched up, should the model turn out to appear too implausible (in the eyes of the sceptic) then, in the absence of viable alternatives, its demise may well result in the subsequent rejection also of the Bible which it purported to support.

Second, caution must be taken to avoid falling into the trap of justifying faith in the Bible on the basis of our ability to provide 'scientific explanations' of biblical events. An instructive historical illustration of this is given by D. C. Allen in his book *The Legend of Noah*.[1] In the seventeenth century, theologians were asked many scientific questions regarding the Flood. The Roman Catholic theologians met scientific difficulties by declaring that the impossibility of

[1] *The Legend of Noah: Renaissance Rationalism in Art, Science, and Letters,* Urbana: University of Illinois Press, 1963.

explaining the mechanics of the Flood clearly showed that it was a miracle. But the Protestants, being anxious to prove that all of the Bible accorded with human reason, tried to work out precise scientific solutions. Their failure to explain the details to the satisfaction of the critics eventually led many to reclassify the inspired history of Noah as simply a myth.

Third, we should not forget that, if a scientific model is to be judged acceptable by the unbeliever, then it must satisfy criteria set *by him*. Since such standards are bound to be at heart unbiblical, the verdict is a foregone conclusion. Those who have rejected God can hardly be expected to evaluate his Word objectively.

For example, the real difficulty that many scientists have with creationists is not so much with the *ad hoc* nature of their theories as with their prior acceptance of the Bible and the restraints it imposes on theorizing. Consider, for example, the words of Michael Ruse, a prominent spokesman for evolutionary science:

> The major reason why Creation-science is not genuine science is that its supporters have to believe, without question or dispute, in the literal truth of Genesis.[1]

Clearly the basic issue here is one of religious presuppositions.

Finally, the above apologetic might be seen as implying that the unbeliever is justified in rejecting Scripture until acceptable scientific explanations of it have been established. What must rather be done is to confront the unbeliever with God's Word and the need for repentance. The biblical data must be adopted as basic, as nonnegotiable articles of faith. The trustworthiness of God's Word must not be made contingent upon our ability to explain it or prove it 'reasonable' by human standards.

Let the onus be on those who reject the accuracy of the Bible to demonstrate the alleged impossibility of biblical events. And if the biblical data are not readily explicable in terms of a scientific model, this should merely serve to illustrate the inadequacy of human theorizing. Our theories must be judged in the light of Scripture, rather than *vice versa*. Let us therefore stress that our prime allegiance is to God and his Word, rather than to any human, scientific explanation of any portions of it.

---

[1] *But Is It Science?*, Buffalo: Prometheus Books, 1988, p. 393.

The Status of Biblical Cosmology

It may be thought that, since biblical cosmologies are presumably based on divinely revealed truth, they are therefore more likely to be right than other cosmological models. The difficulty, however, is that we are blessed with an embarrassment of riches: it is possible to develop not merely one, but a virtually unlimited number of biblically-based cosmologies. The requirement that theories be consistent with Scripture in effect merely expands the data base that the theories must satisfy. As we saw earlier, any number of cosmologies can be constructed to account for the observational data. Thus the problem is not one of constructing a biblical cosmology, but of choosing the correct (or most nearly correct) model from a wide range of possibilities. Again it boils down to a question of constructing and justifying proper criteria for theory selection. In this matter the Bible gives us little help.

In short, while those cosmologies that contradict Scripture are certainly false, biblical cosmologies, to the extent that they go beyond the Bible and observation, are still probably wrong. The speculative nature of scientific theorizing cautions against placing undue trust in any particular model. Let us therefore not be tied down unnecessarily: any theory in harmony with Scripture may possibly be true, although the odds are against it. Any biblical cosmology should therefore be prudently presented as merely a hypothetical possibility, rather than as *the* solution.

This being the case, it is perhaps better to sketch out half a dozen possibilities than to stake too much upon one detailed theory. Such a multiple-theory approach to origins carries with it a number of advantages. The multiple-model approach has more chances of finding good possibilities and underlines the fact that the observational data can be interpreted in many different ways. It cautions against accepting any model as the final truth. It emphasizes the subjective, conjectural element in model building, as well as the great gap between observational data and theories that claim to explain that data.

Thus, for example, with regard to the light-travel-time problem, it should be stressed that many possible solutions exist: perhaps light was created *en route*, perhaps space is curved, perhaps the speed of light is time-dependent or space-dependent. No doubt other possible solutions can be constructed. Which one is right? Only God knows, and beyond that which he has revealed – through direct observation and through his Word – we can only guess.

A better defence of the faith against secular science is, not a demonstration of how well the Bible fits in with human theories and standards, but, rather, an exposure of the limitations of scientific theorizing, particularly with regard to origins. More attention should be focused on the underlying philosophical questions. Here devastating offensives can be mounted against the alleged reliability of secular origin-science. The secular scientific community should be challenged to acknowledge the highly subjective nature of theory construction, selection, and justification; to concede the major role in science played by religious and philosophical presuppositions; and to be less dogmatic about pronouncements regarding origins.

Geisler and Anderson have made the distinction between *origin* science and *operation* science.[1] The latter is concerned with repeatable events, the former with singularities such as creation. I believe this difference to be very important. Christians often justify scientific investigation by referring to the cultural mandate of Genesis 1:28, where man is exhorted to subdue and have dominion over the earth. But the emphasis here is on practical application rather than theoretical knowledge. To be sure, man must first investigate nature before he can develop and regulate it. Yet the text implies that man's ultimate task in science is not to speculate on a hidden reality but to provide useful results. Thus operation science is certainly justified by the cultural mandate, in so far as its goal is that of useful application.

Origin science, on the other hand, is chiefly concerned with conjectures about the distant past. Given the speculative, unverifiable nature of its theories, I question its value. In the absence of objective, valid epistemological criteria that would enable us to detect true theories of origins, origin science can be rated little better than an amusing intellectual parlour game: fun to play, perhaps, but hardly deserving of too much devotion. Note, too, that Scripture has little positive to say about man's theoretical speculations: Job 38-41, on the contrary, stresses man's ignorance regarding origins and deeper questions of nature. That being so, I would suggest that scientists

---

[1] N. L. Geisler and J. K. Anderson, *Origin Science: A Proposal for the Creation-Evolution Controversy*, Grand Rapids: Baker Book House, 1987.

should concentrate on operation science, with the prime aim of developing useful technology.

In summary, biblical cosmologies involve, to a large extent, various features that are inherently unobservable. Although one could construct more detailed models with definite observational predictions, these have only a limited value. The lack of valid criteria for theory selection makes also these Bible-based cosmologies speculative. We should be very much aware of the limitations of scientific extrapolations and explanations, taking care to place our trust in the Word of God rather than in human theorizing.

9

Conclusions

We have come to the end of our study of the interaction between cosmology and theology. Let us summarize the main conclusions reached and make some final comments.

Summary

1. Basic Questions

In our preliminary considerations we discussed the nature of scientific theorizing, as well as various approaches to reconciling science and Scripture. This set the stage for the following chapters. A number of major conclusions can be formulated:

1.1 *The subjectivity of scientific theorizing.*

Scientific theorizing is subjective, and a large role is played in theory selection by extra-scientific presuppositions determined by prior worldview and religious commitments.

1.2 *The limitation of scientific 'facts' to confirmed observations.*

Consequently, in solving the problem of scientific knowledge, only direct, confirmed observations can be considered to constitute scientific 'facts'.

1.3 *The supremacy of God's Word in a Christian epistemology.*

A Christian epistemology should give prime weight to Scripture, deductive logic, and observation. These can be considered to be essentially God-given, and should be consistent. Scientific theorizing, on the other hand, is a fallible human activity that is to be evaluated in the light of the higher epistemic sources.

1.4 Implications of a high view of Scripture.

The epistemic supremacy of Scripture implies that it be considered as inerrant, with full authority, and interpreted via hermeneutical principles consistent with the above epistemology. We should take the Bible in its most direct, literal sense, unless internal scriptural evidence shows conclusively that a non-literal interpretation is required.

2. Historical Cosmology

After a brief overview of ancient cosmology, the focus was on medieval models of the universe. The main lessons learned were:

2.1 The danger of tying theology to a specific cosmology.

Our study of medieval cosmology stressed the danger of combining Christian theology with Aristotelian cosmology. The demise of the latter caused many to modify their Christian theology.

2.2 The elusive nature of absolute motion.

Science can measure only relative motion. The determination of an absolute standard of rest depends on philosophical/theological considerations and definitions. Galileo erred in his claim that he had proved the earth to move in an absolute sense. The widespread, but erroneous, notion that Galileo was right has had profound implications for Christian epistemology and biblical hermeneutics.

3. Modern Cosmology

Our survey of modern cosmology yielded the following main conclusions:

3.1 Shortcomings of big-bang cosmology.

Big-bang cosmology has many serous observational and theoretical deficiencies.

3.2 The possibility of alternative cosmologies.

Cosmological observational data have multiple theoretical interpretations, leading to a host of alternative cosmologies.

3.3 *The necessity of extra-scientific presuppositions.*

Any cosmological model must necessarily rest on various assumptions that are essentially unverifiable. The justification of these basic presuppositions must come from subjective, extra-scientific considerations. We construct cosmological models that are consistent with our most basic philosophical and religious convictions.

4. *Proofs for the Existence of God*

The uncertainty of cosmological models limits their value in arguments purporting to prove the existence of God. In particular, we found:

4.1 *Deficiencies in the cosmological argument.*

The finite past of the universe cannot be conclusively proven through purely philosophical or scientific arguments. Philosophical arguments against the existence of an actual infinity were found to be flawed. Neither big-bang cosmology, even if true, nor the Second Law of Thermodynamics, even if universally applicable, necessarily require the universe to have a finite past.

4.2 *Deficiencies in the design argument.*

The apparent fine-tuning of the universe seems to be much more plausibly explained by divine design than by the alternative explanations of many-world theories, anthropic principles, theories of everything, or natural selection. Yet, this argument, too, lacks compulsion. Criteria such as simplicity and plausibility are often in the eye of the beholder, a beholder whose assessment of competing explanations is shaped by his deepest religious convictions.

4.3 *The God of the proofs and the God of the Bible.*

Even if these theistic proofs were valid, it is still a long way from an abstract First Cause or Prime Mover to the living God of Abraham, Isaac and Jacob. Natural theology is severely limited in its attempts to describe God.

4.4 *The danger of commitment to big-bang cosmology.*

One must be cautious in using big-bang cosmology in theistic proofs. This cosmology may well be dethroned at some future time. Also, the implicit endorsement of big-bang cosmology ushers in a new epistemology that gives too great a weight to speculative theorizing, with grave implications for biblical authority and hermeneutics.

4.5 The limited extent of general revelation.

Big-bang cosmology cannot be equated with revealed truth. God's general revelation through nature concerns only some of God's attributes and is acquired through our direct experience of nature. No biblical evidence suggests that God reveals himself through fallible human theorizing. Rather, the Bible stresses the limitations of human knowledge, particularly regarding origins.

5. Life in the Universe

5.1 The evidence against extra-terrestrials.

We saw that there is no scientific evidence for any natural extra-terrestrial life. Theological considerations weigh heavily against the existence of natural extra-terrestrial intelligence. The uniqueness of Christ's incarnation implies that, if other species do exist, they must be either unfallen or, if fallen, unredeemed.

5.2 Life in a naturalistic universe is doomed.

Modern naturalistic cosmology paints a grim picture of the future of life in the universe: it is doomed to extinction either in a Big Crunch or in a 'heat death'. There is a most pronounced clash between the eschatological predictions of big-bang cosmology and those of the Bible.

6. The Gods of Modern Cosmology

Various attempts to reconcile modern cosmology with religion were examined.

6.1 Big-bang cosmology excludes God and an after-life.

Modern cosmology cannot easily accommodate two of the most essential ingredients for true religion: a supernatural God and subjective immortality. To preserve these fundamental features there must be a spiritual realm wherein God and the soul can exist. Knowledge of such a transcendent realm is necessarily beyond the scrutiny of scientists.

7. The Bible on Cosmology
The teaching of the Bible with respect to cosmology was examined. It was found that the Bible says little regarding the present physical constitution of the universe. Rather, it speaks primarily about the origin and destiny of the universe, as well as its relationship to God.

7.1 The traditional interpretation of Genesis is to be preferred.
Regarding origins, to the extent that challenges to the traditional reading of Genesis are based primarily on extra-biblical considerations, the above epistemology and hermeneutics render these invalid. It follows that the traditional, literal reading of Genesis is the preferred interpretation.

7.2 The recent creation of the universe.
A literal reading of Genesis 1–11, with creation days as normal days and chronologically-complete genealogies in Genesis 5 and 11, places the creation of the world about six thousand years ago.

7.3 The existence of a spiritual realm.
A major feature of a Christian cosmology must be the proper recognition of the spiritual world, extending beyond the usual three spatial dimensions visible to us, with its possible interactions with our physical universe. Heaven has both spatial and temporal aspects.

7.4 A geocentric frame of reference.
The biblical frame of reference is clearly geocentric. However, this has no necessary observational or scientific consequences.

7.5 Big-bang cosmology contradicts the Bible.
A major conclusion of this book is the conflict between big-bang cosmology and the Bible. They clash not only regarding origins, but also regarding eschatology and the existence of spiritual entities. Acceptance of big-bang cosmology has significant implications for Christianity.

8. Biblical Cosmologies
Various Bible-based cosmologies, along with their apologetic values, were examined.

8.1 Limits of young-universe cosmologies.

All such cosmologies ultimately draw upon the concept of mature creation. Although this notion is logically, observationally and theologically unassailable, it offers little in the way of detailed explanations for specific features of astronomical observations. However, truthfulness is more important than broad, but illusory, explanatory powers.

8.2 Limits of geometric cosmologies.

All of the geometric models point to a larger reality beyond that of the physically-observed universe. Their main feature is the affirmation of theological truths, particularly the existence of a spiritual realm. Yet these models offer us little in the way of distinct predictions for physical cosmology.

8.3 Shortcomings of cosmological apologetics.

The construction of biblical cosmologies, showing the Bible to be consistent with our observed universe, may serve to bolster the faith of Christians. However, their apologetic value is rather limited: faith in the Bible must not depend upon our ability to provide acceptable scientific explanations of biblical events. Should the model be deemed inadequate, its demise may well result in the subsequent rejection also of the Bible which it purported to support.

8.4 The limited nature of biblical cosmologies.

An unlimited number of cosmologies can be constructed to account for the biblical and observational data. The lack of valid criteria for theory selection cautions against placing undue trust in any particular model. Any biblical cosmology should therefore be carefully presented as merely a hypothetical possibility, rather than as *the* solution. A multiple-theory approach to origins is more prudent than staking all on one particular theory.

8.5 A preferred apologetic approach.

A better defence of the faith against naturalism is an exposure of the limitations of scientific theorizing, particularly regarding origins. We should stress the highly subjective nature of theory construction, selection, and justification, as well as the major role in science played by religious and philosophical presuppositions.

8.6 Origin and operation science.

Origin science, with its subjective theories and unverifiable conjectures about the distant past, is of questionable value. Scientists should concentrate on operation science, concerned with the practical application of repeatable phenomena, with the prime aim of developing useful technology.

Final Concluding Remarks

1. The Limits of Human Knowledge

The central thesis of this study is that of the severe limitations of human reasoning, particularly scientific theorizing as applied to cosmology. Only direct, confirmed observational data can be accepted as genuine, undoubted 'facts'.

Consequently, much of this investigation has been a rather negative debunking of various conclusions of scientific theorizing. Big-bang cosmology, the current favourite, was the focus of most of our criticism. This was only fitting, as many writers have used it either to discredit or to bolster Christianity. However, alternative cosmologies, including biblically-based cosmologies, were also found to have their shortcomings.

The reader may well feel that I have gone too far, that I have been too sceptical of the veracity of scientific theories. Indeed, most scientists would like scientific 'facts' to include at least some 'well-established' theories. But which ones? How can we determine which theories are more likely to be true? Surely not by a mere majority vote. But what criteria should then be used? And by what criteria should we choose the criteria?

To those who wish to expand the scope of scientific knowledge I leave the challenge of establishing and justifying suitable criteria for discerning true theories. This has yet to be done.

2. The Supremacy of God's Word

Our second prime thesis is that the Bible is God's Word. As such, it is fully authoritative and must be interpreted accordingly. Consequently, a Christian epistemology must insist that fallible, human theorizing is to be evaluated in its light, rather than *vice versa*. Applied consistently, this leaves us with, among other things, the traditional, literal reading of Genesis 1–11.

Again, the reader may feel that I have gone too far. Nowadays few Christian academics are willing to take Genesis at face value. Most, not fully appreciative of the above limitations of science, have become convinced, perhaps, of a vast age of the earth, big-bang cosmology, or the evolutionary origin of man. Since none of these is directly observable, they have in effect elevated particular theoretical conclusions to the status of truth. In doing so they have also, unwittingly perhaps, bought into a secular epistemology that places too great a weight on human theorizing.

Their unduly inflated set of scientific 'facts', placed on a par with Scripture, forces more congenial interpretations of the biblical text. A fallacious epistemology begets a dubious hermeneutic. Further, if naturalistic science can dictate new interpretations of Scripture at one point, such as Genesis 1, why not at other points as well? A hermeneutics bowing to naturalistic science, consistently applied, empties the Bible of all supernatural content.

Of course, any Christian must draw the line at some point, salvaging what are deemed to be essential parts of Christianity. No Christian, for example, could follow the full implications of naturalistic big-bang cosmology and deny a life hereafter. Yet such meagre allowance for mere vestiges of Christianity seems rather contrived: theistic after-thoughts riding on an otherwise naturalist bandwagon. The criteria for biblical interpretation are then driven by subjective assessments of what is and what is not essential Christian doctrine, rather than by a full recognition of and submission to the divine Author.

To those who wish to reject the traditional reading of Genesis 1–11, I leave the challenge of justifying such rejection in terms of valid hermeneutical principles consistent with a Christian epistemology based on the supremacy of God's Word.

3. A Choice of Worldviews

Given the subjective nature of theorizing, and the need of extra-scientific presuppositions, it is clear that one's cosmology is very much determined by one's starting point.

Those who assume that the physical universe is all that exists will prefer a naturalistic cosmology of purely physical causes and effects.

Big-bang cosmology is the creation myth of naturalism. The naturalist, rejecting the supernatural from the start, will, of course, never deem any biblical cosmology to be acceptable. In practice current naturalistic explanations of the observed universe seem highly implausible and have huge gaps. It might be thought that, at least in principle, any defects in the naturalist worldview might eventually be remedied. Yet, even if naturalism could be formulated as a self-consistent worldview, it would give a rather truncated, impoverished view of the world. It has no place for God, the spiritual realm, or life after death. Mind, thoughts, and choices are reduced to mere illusions, thin shadows with no effect on the material world, whose form and contents are completely dependent upon a deterministic, material brain, the accidental result of blind chance.

We are left with a material world void of any values or purpose, a world with no beauty, no justice, no eternal truths and no love. G. K. Chesterton in his book *Orthodoxy* compares the materialist to a madman:

> As an explanation of the world, materialism has a sort of insane simplicity. It has just the quality of the madman's argument; we have at once the sense of covering everything and the sense of leaving everything out . . . He (the materialist) understands everything, and everything does not seem worth understanding. His cosmos may be complete in every rivet and cog-wheel, but still his cosmos is smaller than our world. Somehow his scheme, like the lucid scheme of our madman, seems unconscious of the alien energies and the large indifference of the earth; it is not thinking of the real things of the earth, of fighting peoples or proud mothers, or first love or fear of the sea.[1]

Such is the consistent worldview of naturalism. Its circle of explanations may be complete, but it is a very small circle that traverses only a tiny subset of reality.

The alternative is to start off with God as the ultimate reality. Since God is pure spirit, the spiritual realm now becomes of prime importance. The physical universe, a creation of God, is then reduced to a mere sub-space of a much larger reality. A recognition of spiritual forces interacting with the physical universe readily accounts for the existence of miracles. Even the colossal miracle of

[1] London: Hodder and Stoughton, 1908; reprinted 1996.

the instantaneous creation of the entire physical universe, by a mere word of God, poses no problem.

If God is our starting point, then his revealed Word will also be given the utmost confidence as the only trustworthy source of knowledge beyond our observational horizon. Through it we acquire knowledge of God, of his plan for the universe, of the spiritual realm, and of moral standards. In short, theism can easily give a plausible explanation for the observed world, as well as the existence of such things as mind, purpose, values, sin and love. From the theistic perspective, the fact that naturalistic science contradicts the Bible merely indicates the inadequacy of human thought left to itself. Though theism's explanations are still incomplete, its depiction of reality is a much fuller one than that of naturalism.

The choice is clear: either naturalism is true, and the biblical conception of reality is an illusion, or the Bible is true and naturalism, including its big-bang myth of origins, must be rejected as mere fantasy.

4. A Plea for Consistency

As Christians we must constantly be on guard not to be conformed to the world but, rather, to be transformed in our every thought. We must work out the full consequences of our faith in fear and trembling, resisting pressures to compromise. Also, in scientific matters, we should be careful to uphold our Christian values and epistemology, thoroughly examining scientific claims before accepting them.

In recent years there has been a significant increase in the recognition given to Christian scholars by secular institutions. Nevertheless, the question has been raised as to whether such evangelical scholarship has been acknowledged only to the extent that it has become secularized. Craig M. Gay suggests that this recognition may well be due to Christian scholars increasingly adopting the secular academic community as their reference point over against that of the believing community.[1]

There has been much stress among Christian academics on the integration of faith and science. Yet such integration often seems to consist more in accommodating Christianity to one's discipline than

[1] 'The Uneasy Intellect of Modern Evangelicalism', *Crux,* 1990, *xxvi,* pp. 8–11.

vice versa. More attention should perhaps be paid to *differentiation* rather than *integration*. Christian scholars need to examine much more critically the methodology, epistemology and contents of their various disciplines. Each discipline should be dismantled, starting at the foundation, purged of unbiblical notions, and rebuilt in accordance with biblical values and givens. Only thus can genuine integration be attained.

Regarding cosmology in particular, it is clear that, if we are to save such Christian essentials as the return of Christ and a life hereafter, then at some point we must break with big-bang cosmology. If, then, ultimately we will be fools in the eyes of the world anyway, why not at least be consistent fools, and uphold God's Word in its undiminished entirety?

In this life we must acknowledge our human limitations, particularly with regard to scientific knowledge. Since the Bible is our only source of absolute truth, it is better to take it too seriously – if that can ever be done! – than to risk compromising it, however good our intentions may be. Let us therefore hold fast to God's Word – neither adding to it nor subtracting from it – and construct our cosmological theories accordingly, striving to make every thought captive to Christ.

Bibliography

ABDELKADER, MOSTAFA A., 'A Geocosmos: Mapping Outer Space into a Hollow Earth', *Speculations in Science and Technology,* 1983, 6, pp. 81–9.

ABBOTT, EDWIN A., *Flatland,* 1844, repr. New York: Dover, 1992.

ALBRECHT, ANDREAS and JOAO MAGUEIJO, 'A Time Varying Speed of Light as a Solution to Cosmological Problems', *Physical Review,* 1999, D 59: 043516.

ALFVEN, HANNES O. G., 'Cosmology: Myth or Science?', *in* W. Yourgrau and A. D. Breck (eds.), *Cosmology, History, and Theology,* New York: Plenum Press, 1974.

ALLEN, D. C., *The Legend of Noah: Renaissance Rationalism in Art, Science, and Letters,* Urbana: University of Illinois Press, 1963.

ANDREWS, E. H., *in* O. R. Barclay (ed.), *Creation & Evolution: When Christians Disagree,* Downers Grove: InterVarsity Press, 1985.

ARP, HALTON, *Seeing Red,* Montreal: Apeiron, 1998.

ARP, HALTON, ROY KEYS, and KONRAD RUDNICKI, *Progress in New Cosmologies: Beyond the Big Bang,* New York: Plenum Press, 1993.

BARBOUR, IAN G., *Issues in Science and Religion,* New York: Harper, 1971.

BARBOUR, IAN G., *Religion in an Age of Science,* San Francisco: Harper, 1990.

BARBOUR, J. B. and B. BERTOTTI, 'Gravity and Inertia in a Machian Framework', *Il Nuovo Cimento,* 1977, B 38, pp. 1–28.

BARROW, JOHN D., *The World within the World,* Oxford: Clarendon Press, 1988.

BARROW, JOHN D., 'Cosmologies with Varying Light-Speed', *Physical Review,* 1999, D 59: 043515.

BARROW, JOHN D. and FRANK J. TIPLER, *The Anthropic Cosmological Principle,* Oxford: The University Press, 1986.

BERKHOF, LOUIS, *Systematic Theology,* London: Banner of Truth, 1958.

BERLINSKI, DAVID, 'Was There a Big Bang?', *Commentary Magazine,* February 1998. See also 'Letters from Readers' and Berlinski's response in *Commentary Magazine,* May 1998.

BLOCHER, HENRI, *In the Beginning,* Downers Grove: Inter-Varsity Press, 1984.

BOSLOUGH, JOHN, *Stephen Hawking's Universe,* New York: William Morrow, 1985.

BOUW, GERARDUS D., 'Geocentricity in the Twentieth Century?', *Bulletin of the Tychonian Society,* 1988, 46, p. 32.

BOUW, GERARDUS D., *Geocentricity*, Cleveland: Association for Biblical Astronomy, 1992.

BRAUN, FRITZ, *Das Drei-Stockige Weltall der Bibel*, Salem-Obw.: Morgenland Verlag, 1973; also available in English as *Space and the Universe*.

BURBIDGE, G., 'Modern Cosmology: the Harmonious and the Discordant Facts', *in* B. R. Iyer (ed.), *Highlights in Gravitation and Cosmology*, Cambridge: The University Press, 1988.

BURBIDGE, G. and F. HOYLE, 'The Origin of Helium and the Other Light Elements', *Astrophysical Journal*, 1998, 509, pp. L1–3.

BURBIDGE, G., F. HOYLE and J. V. NARLIKAR, 'A Different Approach to Cosmology', *Physics Today*, 1999, 52 (April), pp. 38–44.

BURLES, SCOTT, et al., 'Sharpening the Predictions of Big-Bang Nucleosynthesis', *Physical Review Letters*, 1999, 82, pp. 4176–9.

BYL, JOHN, 'Instrumentalism: A Third Option', *Journal of the American Scientific Affiliation*, 1985, 37, pp. 11–18.

BYL, JOHN, 'On Small Curved-Space Models of the Universe', *Creation Research Society Quarterly*, 1988, 25, pp. 138–40.

BYL, JOHN, 'General Revelation and Evangelicalism', *Mid-America Journal of Theology*, 1989, 5, pp. 1–13.

BYL, JOHN, 'On the Natural Selection of Universes', *Quarterly Journal of the Royal Astronomical Society*, 1996, 37, pp. 369–71.

BYL, JOHN, 'The Role of Beliefs in Modern Cosmology', in J. M. van der Meer (ed.), *Facets of Faith and Science*, Lanham: University Press of America, 1996, Vol. 3, pp. 47–62.

BYL, JOHN, 'On Craig's Defence of the KalamCosmological Argument', in J. M. van der Meer (ed.), *Facets of Faith and Science*, Lanham: University Press of America, 1996, Vol. 4, pp. 75–90.

BYL, JOHN, 'On Time Dilation in Cosmology', *Creation Research Society Quarterly*, 1997, 34, pp. 26–32.

CALVIN, JOHN, *Institutes of the Christian Religion*, 1559 edition.

CAMERON, A. G. W., *Interstellar Communication*, New York: Benjamin, 1963.

CHESTERTON, G. K., *Orthodoxy*, London: Hodder and Stoughton, 1908.

CLARK, G. H., *Thales to Dewey*, Grand Rapids: Baker Book House, 1957.

CLOUSER, ROY A., *The Myth of Religious Neutrality*, Notre Dame, Ind.: University of Notre Dame, 1991.

CLUBE, S. V. M., 'The Material Vacuum', *Monthly Notices of the Royal Astronomical Society*, 1980, 193, p. 385.

COBB, JOHN B., *A Christian Natural Theology*, Philadelphia: Westminster Press, 1965.

Cobb, John B., *Christ in a Pluralistic Age*, Philadelphia: Westminster Press, 1975.

Coles, P., 'The End of the Old Model Universe', *Nature, 393* (25 June 1998), p. 741.

Cooper, John W., *Body, Soul, and Life Everlasting*, Grand Rapids: Eerdmans, 1989.

Craig, W. L., *The Kalam Cosmological Argument*, London: Macmillan, 1979.

Craig, W. L., 'Philosophical and Scientific Pointers to Creation Ex Nihilo', *Journal of the American Scientific Affiliation*, 1980, *32*, pp. 5–13.

Craig, W. L., 'Hugh Ross's Extra-Dimensional Deity: A Review Article', *Journal of the Evangelical Theological Society*, 1999, *42*, pp. 293–304.

Crawford, David F., 'A New Gravitational Interaction of Cosmological Importance', *Astrophysical Journal*, 1991, *377*, pp. 1–6.

Crawford, David F., 'A Static Stable Universe', *Astrophysical Journal*, 1993, *410*, pp. 488–92.

Crawford, Ian, 'Galactic Civilizations: A Reply', *Astronomy & Geophysics*, 1997, *38*, p. 19.

Darwin, Charles, *On the Origin of the Species*, 2nd ed., London: John Murray, 1859.

Davidson, H. A., *Proofs for Eternity, Creation and the Existence of God in Medieval Islamic and Jewish Philosophy*, Oxford: The University Press, 1987.

Davies, Paul, *God and the New Physics*, New York: Simon & Schuster, 1983.

Davies, Paul, *The Cosmic Blueprint*, New York: Simon & Schuster, 1988.

Davies, Paul, *Are We Alone? Philosophical Implications of the Discovery of Extraterrestrial Life*, New York: Basic Books, 1995.

Davis, J. J., 'Search for Extraterrestrial Intelligence and the Christian Doctrine of Redemption', *Science & Christian Belief*, 1997, *9*, pp. 21–34.

De Sitter, W., 'The Evolution of the Universe', *Nature*, 1931, *128*, p. 707.

De Young, Don B., *Astronomy and the Bible*, Grand Rapids: Baker Book House, 1989.

Dick, Steven J., *Plurality of Worlds*, Cambridge: The University Press, 1981.

Diehl, David W., 'Evangelicalism and General Revelation: An Unfinished Agenda', *Journal of the Evangelical Theological Society*, 1987, *30*, p. 441.

Dillenberger, John, *Protestant Thought and Natural Science*, New York: Abingdon Press, 1960.

Dingle, H., 'Philosophical Aspects of Cosmology', *Vistas in Astronomy*, 1960, *1*, p. 166.

DREES, WILLEM B., *Beyond the Big Bang: Quantum Cosmologies and God*, Th.D. Thesis, Rijksuniversiteit Groningen, The Netherlands, 1989.

DYSON, F., *Disturbing the Universe*, New York: Harper and Row, 1979.

DYSON, F., *Infinite in All Directions*, New York: Harper and Row, 1988.

EARMAN, JOHN and JESUS MOSTERIN, 'A Critical Look at Inflationary Cosmology', *Philosophy of Science*, 1999, 66, pp. 1–49.

EDDINGTON, A. S., *The Internal Constitution of the Stars*, Cambridge: The University Press, 1926.

EDDINGTON, A. S., *The Nature of the Physical World*, 1928, repr. Ann Arbor: University of Michigan, 1963.

EINSTEIN, ALBERT, *The Meaning of Relativity*, 5th Edition, Princeton: The University Press, 1956.

EINASTO, J., et al., 'A 120-Mpc Periodicity in the Three-dimensional Distribution of Galaxy Superclusters', *Nature*, 1997, *385*, p. 139.

ELLIS, G. F. R., 'Cosmology and Verifiability', *Quarterly Journal of the Royal Astronomical Society*, 1975, *16*, pp. 245–64.

ELLIS, G. F. R., 'Is the Universe Expanding?', *General Relativity and Gravitation*, 1978, *9*, pp. 87–94.

ELLIS, G. F. R., 'Alternatives to the Big Bang', *Annual Review of Astronomy & Astrophysics*, 1984, *22*, pp. 157–84.

ELLIS, G. F. R., 'Piety in the Sky', *Nature*, 1994, *371*, p. 115.

ELLIS, G. F. R. and D. H. COULE, 'Life at the End of the Universe', *General Relativity and Gravitation*, 1994, *26*, pp. 713–39.

FINLAY-FREUNDLICH, E., 'Red Shifts in the Spectrum of Celestial Bodies', *Philosophical Magazine*, 1954, *45*, pp. 303–19.

FISCHER, E., 'A Cosmological Model without Singularity', *Astrophysics and Space Science*, 1993, *206*, pp. 203–19.

FLEMING, K. C., *God's Voice in the Stars: Zodiac Signs and Bible Truth*, Neptune, N.J.: Loizeau Brothers, 1981.

GALILEO GALILEI, 'Letter to the Grand Duchess Christina' (1615), in *Discoveries and Opinions of Galileo*, translated by Stillman Drake, New York: Doubleday Anchor, 1957.

GAMOW, G., 'Modern Cosmology', *Scientific American*, 1954, *190*, pp. 55–63.

GAY, CRAIG M., 'The Uneasy Intellect of Modern Evangelicalism', *Crux*, 1990, xxvi, pp. 8–11.

GEISLER, NORMAN L., *Journal of the Evangelical Theological Society*, 1979, 22, p. 282.

GEISLER, NORMAN L., *Knowing the Truth About Creation*, Ann Arbor: Servant Books, 1989.

GEISLER, NORMAN L. and J. K. ANDERSON, *Origin Science: A Proposal for the Creation-Evolution Controversy*, Grand Rapids: Baker Book House, 1987.

GEISLER, NORMAN L. AND W. CORDUAN, *Philosophy of Religion,* Grand Rapids: Baker, 1988.

GELLER, M. J. and J. P. HUCHRA, 'Cosmic Cartographers Find 'Great Wall'', *Science News,* 1989, *136*, p. 340.

GENTRY, ROBERT, 'A New Redshift Interpretation', *Modern Physics Letters A,* 1997, *12*, p. 2919.

GREEN, W. H., *Bibliotheca Sacra,* 1890, *47*, pp. 285–303, reprinted as an Appendix in R. C. Newman and H. J. Eckelmann, *Genesis One and the Age of the Earth,* Downers Grove: InterVarsity Press, 1977.

GHOSH, A.,'Velocity-Dependent Inertial Induction: a Possible Tired-Light Mechanism', *Apeiron,* 1991, *9-10*, pp. 35–44.

GILMORE, G., et al., 'First Detection of Beryllium in a Very Metal-Poor Star: a Test of the Standard Big Bang Model', *Astrophysical Journal,* 1991, *378*, pp. 17–21.

GLANZ, JAMES, 'Worlds Around Other Stars Shake Planet Birth Theory', *Science,* 1997, *276*, pp. 1336–9.

GRIBBIN, JOHN, 'Bunched Redshifts Question Cosmology', *New Scientist,* 1991, *132*, pp. 1800–1.

GRUNBAUM, ADOLPH, 'The Pseudo-Problem of Creation in Physical Cosmology', *Philosophy of Science,* 1989, *56*, pp. 373–94.

GUTH, A. H. and M. SHER, 'The Impossibility of a Bouncing Universe', *Nature,* 1983, *302*, pp. 505–7.

HARRISON, EDWARD R., *Cosmology: The Science of the Universe*, Cambridge: The University Press, 1981.

HARRISON, EDWARD R., 'The Natural Selection of Universes Containing Intelligent Life', *Quarterly Journal of the Royal Astronomical Society,* 1995, *36*, pp. 193–203.

HART, MICHAEL H., *Extraterrestrials – Where are They?* New York: Pergamon Press, 1982.

HARTSHORNE, CHARLES, *The Logic of Perfection*, LaSalle, Ill.: Open Court, 1962.

HAWKING, S. W., *A Brief History of Time*, New York: Bantam, 1988.

HAWKING, S. W. and G. F. R. ELLIS, 'The Cosmic Black-Body Radiation and the Existence of Singularities in Our Universe', *Astrophysical Journal,* 1967, *152*, pp. 25–35.

HAWKING, S. W. and R. PENROSE, 'The Singularities of Gravitational Collapse and Cosmology', *Proc. Royal Society of London,* 1970, *A 314*, pp. 529–48.

HECHT, JEFF, 'Astronomers' Double Whammy Rocks Cosmology', *New Scientist,* 1994, *141,* p. 16.

HEEREN, FRED, *Show Me God: What the Message from Space Is Telling Us about God,* Wheeling: Searchlight, 1995.

HEMPEL, CARL G., *Philosophy of Natural Science,* Englewood Cliffs, N.J.: Prentice-Hall, 1966.

HENNINGER, S.K., *The Cosmological Glass: Renaissance Diagrams of the Universe,* San Marino, Calif.: Huntington Library, 1977.

HORGAN, J., 'Universal Truths', *Scientific American,* Oct. 1990, pp. 109–17.

HOYLE, FRED, *Astronomy and Cosmology,* San Francisco: Freeman, 1975.

HOYLE, FRED, 'On the Origin of the Microwave Background', *Astrophysical Journal,* 1975, *196,* p. 661.

HOYLE, FRED, *Ten Faces of the Universe,* San Francisco: Freeman, 1977.

HOYLE, FRED, *The Intelligent Universe,* New York: Holt, Rinehart and Winston, 1983.

HUMPHREYS, C. J., 'The Star of Bethlehem – a Comet in 5 BC – and the Date of the Birth of Christ', *Quarterly Journal of the Royal Astronomical Society,* 1991, *32,* pp. 389–407.

HUMPHREYS, D. R., *Starlight and Time,* Colorado Springs: Master Books, 1994.

ISRAELIT, M. and N. ROSEN, 'A Singularity-Free Cosmological Model in General Relativity', *Astrophysical Journal,* 1989, *342,* p. 627.

JAGER, OKKE, *Het Eeuwige Leven: Met Name in Verband Met de Verhouding van Tijd en Eeuwigheid,* Kampen: Kok, 1962.

JORDAN, JAMES B., *Creation in Six Days: A Defense of the Traditional Reading of Genesis One,* Moscow, Idaho: Canon Press, 1999.

KANT, IMMANUEL, *Allgemeine Naturgeschichte und Theorie des Himmels* (1755); an English translation by Stanley L. Jaki can be found in Yourgrau and Beck, *Cosmology, History, and Theology* (see ALFVEN reference above).

KELLY, DOUGLAS F., *Creation and Change: Genesis 1.1–2.4 in the Light of Changing Scientific Paradigms,* Tain, Ross-shire: Mentor, 1997.

KIEREIN, J.W., 'A Criticism of Big Bang Cosmological Models Based on Interpretation of the Red Shift', *Laser and Particle Beams,* 1988, *6,* pp. 453-456.

KOESTLER, ARTHUR, *The Sleepwalkers,* Harmondsworth: Penguin, 1968.

KOYRÉ, ALEXANDRE, *From the Closed World to the Infinite Universe,* Baltimore: Johns Hopkins Press, 1957.

KUHN, T. S., *The Copernican Revolution,* Cambridge, Mass.: Harvard University Press, 1957.

LAKATOS, IMRE, *The Methodology of Research Programmes*, Cambridge: The University Press, 1980.

LAUER, T. R. and M. POSTMAN, 'The Motion of the Local Group', *Astrophysical Journal,* 1994, *425,* pp. 418–38.

LA VIOLETTE, PAUL A., *Beyond the Big Bang: Ancient Myth and the Science of Continuous Creation*, Rochester, Vermont: Park Street Press, 1995.

LERNER, E. J., 'Plasma Models of Microwave Background and Primordial Elements: An Alternative to the Big Bang', *Laser and Particle Beams,* 1988 *6*, pp. 456–68.

LERNER, E. J., 'Galactic Model of Element Formation', *IEEE Transactions on Plasma Science,* 1989, *17*, pp. 259–63.

LERNER, E. J., *The Big Bang Never Happened*, New York: Times Books, 1991.

LESLIE, JOHN, 'Modern Cosmology and the Creation of Life', *in* E. McMullin (ed.), *Evolution and Creation*, Notre Dame: University of Notre Dame Press, 1985.

LESLIE, JOHN, *Universes,* London: Routledge, 1989.

LESLIE, JOHN (ed.), *Physical Cosmology and Philosophy*, London, 1990.

LEWIS, C. S., *The Discarded Image,* Cambridge: The University Press, 1963.

LEY, W., *Rockets, Missiles, and Space Travel*, New York: Viking Press, 1951.

LIGHTMAN, A. and R. BRAWER, *Origins*, Cambridge, Mass.: Harvard University Press, 1990.

LINDE, ANDREI, 'The Universe: Inflation out of Chaos', *New Scientist,* 7 March 1985, pp. 14–18.

LINDE, ANDREI, 'Particle Physics and Inflationary Cosmology', *Physics Today,* 1987, *40*, pp. 61–8.

LINDE, ANDREI, 'The Self-Reproducing Inflationary Universe', *Scientific American,* Nov. 1994, pp. 48–55.

LINDE, ANDREI, DMITRI LINDE and ARTHUR MEZHLUMIAN, 'Do We Live in the Center of the World?', *Physics Letters,* 1995, *B 345*, pp. 203–10.

LOVEJOY, ARTHUR O., *The Great Chain of Being*, Cambridge, Mass.: Harvard University Press, 1936.

LUBENOW, MARVIN L., *Bones of Contention*, Grand Rapids: Baker, 1992.

LYNDEN-BELL, D., J. KATZ and J. BICAK, 'Mach's Principle from the Relativistic Constraint Equations', *Monthly Notices of the Royal Astronomical Society,* 1995, *272*, pp. 150–60.

MACKAY, D. S. et al., 'Search for Past Life on Mars: Possible Relic Biogenic Activity in Martian Meteorite ALH84001', *Science,* 1996, *273*, pp. 924–30.

MARKOV, M. A., 'Asymptotic Freedom and Entropy in a Perpetually Oscillating Universe', *Physics Letters,* 1983, *94A,* pp. 427–9.

MARKOV, M. A., 'Some Problems of Modern Theory of Gravitation', in *The Past and Future of the Universe,* Moscow: Nauka, 1989, pp.11–23.

MARMET, PAUL and GROTE REBER, 'Cosmic Matter and the Nonexpanding Universe', *IEEE Transactions on Plasma Science,* 1989, *17,* pp. 264–9.

MASCALL, E.L., *Christian Theology and Natural Science,* London: Longmans, Green and Co., 1956.

MARTIN, E. L., *The Birth of Christ Recalculated,* Pasadena: Foundation for Biblical Research, 1980.

MCMULLIN, ERNAN, 'How Should Cosmology Relate to Theology?' *in* A. R. Peacocke, *The Sciences and Theology in the Twentieth Century,* Stocksfield: Oriel Press, 1981.

MENNINGA, CLARENCE, 'Creation, Time, and 'Apparent Age''', *Perspectives on Science and Christian Faith,* 1988, *40,* p. 161.

MILNE, A. E., *Modern Cosmology and the Christian Idea of God,* Oxford: Clarendon Press, 1952.

MITCHEL, W. C., *The Cult of the Big Bang,* Carson City: Cosmic Sense Books, 1995.

MITCHEL, W. C., 'Big Bang Theory Under Fire', *Physics Essays,* 1997, *10,* No.2.

MOON, PARRY and SPENCER, DOMINA E., 'Binary Stars and the Velocity of Light', *Journal of the Optical Society of America,* 1953, *43,* pp. 635–41.

MOON, PARRY and SPENCER, DOMINA E., 'Mach's principle', *Philosophy of Science,* 1959, *26,* pp. 125–34.

MOORE, BEN, 'Evidence Against Dissipationless Dark Matter from Observations of Galaxy Haloes', *Nature,* 1994, *370,* pp. 629–31.

MORELAND, J. P., *The Creation Hypothesis,* Downers Grove: InterVarsity Press, 1994.

MORRIS, HENRY M., *The Twilight of Evolution,* Philadelphia: Presbyterian and Reformed, 1963.

MORRIS, HENRY M., *The Remarkable Birth of Planet Earth,* Minneapolis: Dimension Books, 1972.

MUSSER, GEORGE, 'Glow in the Dark', *Scientific American,* March 1998, *278,* 3, p. 18.

NARLIKAR, J. V., *The Primeval Universe,* Oxford: The University Press, 1968.

NARLIKAR, J. V., 'Did the Universe Originate in a Big Bang?', *in* S. K. Biswas (ed.), *Cosmic Perspectives,* Cambridge: The University Press, 1989.

NASA, 'Hubble Uncovers New Clues to Galaxy Formation', http://opposite.stsci.edu/pubinfo/background-text/galxpdx.txt, 1994.

NASH, R. H., *The Concept of God*, Grand Rapids: Academe Books, 1983.

NATIONAL ACADEMY OF SCIENCE, *Scientific Creationism: A View from the National Academy of Science*, Washington: National Academy Press, 1984.

NIESSEN, RICHARD, 'A Biblical Approach to Dating the Earth: A Case for the Use of Genesis 5 and 11 as an Exact Chronology', *Creation Research Society Quarterly*, 1982, 19, pp. 60–6.

NORMAN, TREVOR and BARRY SETTERFIELD, *The Atomic Constants, Light and Time*, Flinders University, Australia, 1987.

OGDEN, SCHUBERT M., *The Reality of God and Other Essays*, New York: Harper and Row, 1966.

OGDEN, SCHUBERT M., 'The Meaning of Christian Hope', *Union Seminary Quarterly Review*, 1975, *30*, pp. 160–3.

OLDERSHAW, R. L., 'The New Physics – Physical or Mathematical Science?', *American Journal of Physics*, 1988, 56, pp. 1075–81.

OVENDEN, M. W., 'The Origin of the Constellations', *The Philosophical Journal*, 1966, 3, pp. 1–18.

OZANNE, C. G., *The First 7000 Years: A Study in Bible Chronology*, New York: Exposition Press, 1970.

PAGELS, HEINZ R., 'A Cozy Cosmology', *in* LESLIE, *Physical Cosmology and Philosophy*, 1990.

PEACOCK, ROY E., *A Brief History of Eternity*, Wheaton: Crossway Books, 1990.

PEEBLES, P. J. E., Book Review: *Inner Space/Outer Space – The Interface between Cosmology and Particle Physics* by E.W. Kolb, *Science*, 1987, 235, p. 372.

PEEBLES, P. J. E., *Principles of Physical Cosmology*, Princeton: The University Press, 1993.

PENROSE, ROGER, 'Difficulties with Inflationary Cosmology', *Annals of the New York Academy of Sciences*, 1989, 571, pp. 249–64.

PETERS, TED (ed.), *Cosmos as Creation*, Nashville: Abingdon Press, 1989.

PETERS, TED, 'The Trinity in and beyond Time', *in* RUSSELL, MURPHY and ISHAM, 1996.

POE, EDGAR ALLAN, *Eureka: A Prose Poem*, New York: Putnam, 1848.

POLKINGHORNE, JOHN, *One World: The Interaction of Science and Theology*, Princeton: The University Press, 1986.

POLKINGHORNE, JOHN, *Science and Creation*, London: SPCK, 1988.

POLKINGHORNE, JOHN, 'Cross-Traffic Between Science and Theology', *Perspectives on Science and Christian Faith,* 1991, *43,* pp. 144–51.

POLKINGHORNE, JOHN, *The Faith of a Physicist,* Princeton: The University Press, 1994.

POPPER, KARL R., *Conjectures and Refutations,* London: Routledge, 1963.

POPPER, KARL R., *Objective Knowledge,* London: Oxford University Press, 1972.

RAMM, BERNARD, *The Christian View of Science and Scripture,* Grand Rapids: Eerdmans, 1954.

RAO, J. KRISHNA and M. ANNAPURNA, 'Spherically Symmetric Static Inhomogeneous Cosmological Models', *Pramana,* 1991, *36,* pp. 95–103.

REES, MARTIN, 'Ripples from the Edge of Time', *Guardian Weekly,* 3 May 1992, p. 11.

ROSS, HUGH, *The Fingerprint of God,* Orange: Promise Publishing Co., 2nd edition, 1991.

ROSS, HUGH, *The Creator and the Cosmos,* Colorado Springs: Navpress, 1993.

ROSS, HUGH, *Creation and Time,* Colorado Springs: Navpress, 1994.

ROSS, HUGH, *Beyond the Cosmos,* Colorado Springs: Navpress, 1996.

ROSS, HUGH, *The Genesis Question,* Colorado Springs: Navpress, 1998.

ROZENTAL, I. L., *Big Bang, Big Bounce,* Berlin: Springer Verlag, 1988.

RUSE, MICHAEL (ed.), *But Is It Science?* Buffalo: Prometheus Books, 1988.

RUSSELL, BERTRAND, *The ABC of Relativity,* London: Allen and Unwin, 1958.

RUSSELL, J. R. (ed.), *Physics, Philosophy and Theology: A Common Quest for Understanding,* Vatican City: Vatican Observatory Press, 1988.

RUSSELL, J. R., NANCY MURPHY AND C. J. ISHAM (eds.), *Quantum Cosmology and the Laws of Nature: Scientific Perspectives on Divine Action,* Vatican City: Vatican Observatory Publications, 1996.

SAGAN, CARL, *Broca's Brain,* New York: Random House, 1979.

SCHILLING, G., 'Galaxies Seen at the Universe's Dawn', *Science,* 1999, *283,* p. 21.

SCHROEDER, GERALD L., *Genesis and the Big Bang,* New York: Bantam, 1990.

SEGAL, I. E., J. F. NICOLL, P. WU and Z. ZHOU, 'Statistically Efficient Testing of the Hubble and Lundmark Laws on IRAS Galaxy Samples', *Astrophysical Journal,* 1993, *411,* pp. 465–84.

SEGAL, I. E. and Z. ZHOU, 'Maxwell's Equations in the Einstein Universe and Chronometric Cosmology', *Astrophysical Journal Supplement,* 1995, *100,* p. 307.

SEGAL, I. E. and J. F. NICOLL, 'Statistics of a Complete High-Redshift Quasar Survey and Predictions of Nonevolutionary Cosmologies', *Astrophysical Journal,* 1996, *459,* p. 496.

Seiss, J. A., *The Gospel in the Stars*, 1882, repr. Grand Rapids: Kregel, 1972.

Selbrede, M. G., 'Geocentricity's Critics Refuse to Do Their Homework', *Chalcedon Report*, 1994, No. 351, pp. 33–40.

Senovilla, J. M. M., 'Singularity Theorems and Their Consequences', *General Relativity & Gravitation*, 1998, *30*, pp. 701–848.

Setterfield, Barry, 'The Velocity of Light and the Age of the Universe', *Ex Nihilo*, 1981, *4*(1), pp. 38–48, (3), pp. 56–81.

Shull, J. Michael, 'Intergalactic Pollution', *Nature*, 1999, *394*, pp. 17–18.

Smith, Quentin, 'Infinity and the Past', *Philosophy of Science*, 1987, *54*, pp. 63–75.

Smith, Quentin, 'The Uncaused Beginning of the Universe', *Philosophy of Science*, 1988, *55*, pp. 39–57.

Smith, Wilbur M., *The Biblical Doctrine of Heaven*, Chicago: Moody, 1968.

Sorabji, Richard, *Time, Creation and the Continuum*, Ithaca: Cornell University Press, 1983.

Spencer, Stephen R., 'Is Natural Theology Biblical?', *Grace Theological Journal*, 1988, *9*, pp. 59–72.

Stoeger, William, 'Contemporary Cosmology and Implications for the Science-Religion Dialogue', *in* Russell, *Physics, Philosophy and Theology*.

Strauss, M. A. et al., 'Can Standard Cosmological Models Explain the Observed Abell Cluster Bulk Flow?', *Astrophysical Journal*, 1995, *444*, pp. 507–19.

Swinburne, Richard, 'Argument from the Fine-Tuning of the Universe', *in* Leslie, *Physical Cosmology and Philosophy*, 1990.

Teilhard de Chardin, P., *The Phenomenon of Man*, London: Collins, 1959.

Tifft, W. G., 'Global Redshift Periodicities and Periodicity Variability', *Astrophysical Journal*, 1997, *485*, pp. 465–83.

Tipler, Frank J., 'ETI Beings Do Not Exist', *Quarterly Journal of the Royal Astronomical Society*, 1980, *21*, p. 278.

Tipler, Frank J., 'A Brief History of the ETI Concept', *Quarterly Journal of the Royal Astronomical Society*, 1982, 22, pp. 133–45.

Tipler, Frank J., 'How to Construct a Falsifiable Theory in Which the Universe Came into Being Several Thousand Years Ago', *Proceedings of the 1984 Biennial Meeting of the Philosophy of Science Association, Volume II*, East Lansing, Mich.: Philosophy of Science Association, 1984, pp. 873–902.

Tipler, Frank J., 'The Omega Point Theory: A Model of an Evolving God', *in* Russell, *Physics, Philosophy and Theology*.

TIPLER, FRANK J., 'The Omega Point as Eschaton: Answers to Pannenberg's Questions for Scientists', *Zygon,* 1989, *24*, pp. 217–53.

TIPLER, FRANK J., *The Physics of Immortality*, New York: Doubleday, 1994.

TROITSKII, V. S., 'Physical Constants and Evolution of the Universe', *Astrophysics and Space Science,* 1987, *139*, pp. 389–411.

TRYON, EDWARD P., 'Is the Universe a Vacuum Fluctuation?', *Nature,* 1973, *246*, pp. 396–7.

TURNER, MICHAEL S. and ANTHONY TYSON, 'Cosmology at the Millennium', *Reviews of Modern Physics,* 1999, *71*, S145–64.

VAN DEN BROM, L. J., *God Alomtegenwoordig.* Kampen: Kok, 1982.

VAN DEN BROM, L. J., 'Interpreting the Doctrine of Creation', *in* Vincent Brummer (ed.), *Interpreting the Universe as Creation,* Kampen, : Kok Pharos, 1991.

VAN FLANDERN, T., *Dark Matter, Missing Planets and New Comets,* Berkeley, North Atlantic Books, 1993.

VAN TILL, H. J., *The Fourth Day*, Grand Rapids: Eerdmans, 1986.

VAN TILL, H. J., *Portraits of Creation*, Grand Rapids: Eerdmans, 1990.

WEINBERG, STEVEN, *The First Three Minutes*, New York: Bantam Books, 1979.

WEINBERG, STEVEN, *Dreams of a Final Theory*, New York: Pantheon, 1992.

WHITCOMB, JOHN C. and HENRY M. MORRIS, *The Genesis Flood,* Philadelphia: Presbyterian and Reformed, 1961.

WHITE, SIMON D. M. et al., 'The Baryon Content of Galaxy Clusters: A Challenge to Orthodox Cosmology', *Nature,* 1993, *366*, p. 429.

WHITEHEAD, A. N., *Process and Reality*, New York: Macmillan, 1929.

WILDIERS, N. MAX, *The Theologian and His Universe*, New York: Seabury Press, 1982.

YOUNG, DAVIS, *Christianity and the Age of the Earth*, Grand Rapids: Zondervan, 1982.

YOUNG, DAVIS, 'Scripture in the Hands of Geologists', *Westminster Theological Journal,* 1987, *49*, p. 1–34, 257–304.

ZANSTRA, HERMAN, 'Is Religion Refuted by Physics or Astronomy?', *Vistas in Astronomy,* 1968, *10*, pp. 1–21.

ZANSTRA, HERMAN, 'Thermodynamics, Statistical Mechanics, and the Universe? *Vistas in Astronomy,* 1968, *10*, pp. 23–44.

ZEILIK, MICHAEL, *Conceptual Astronomy*, New York: Wiley, 1993.

ZHI, FANG LI and XIAN, LI SHU, *Creation of the Universe.* Singapore: World Scientific, 1989.

Index of Names and Subjects